THE CHAMPLIN FIGHTER
MUSEUM

HOME OF
THE AMERICAN FIGHTER ACES ASSOCIATION AND
THE J. CURTIS EARL AUTOMATIC WEAPONS COLLECTION

Aerofax, Inc. for
**THE CHAMPLIN FIGHTER
MUSEUM PRESS**

Jay Miller/Aerofax, Inc.

Aviatik D.I painting by noted aviation artist Jack Fellows.

Published by Champlin Press
4636 Fighter Aces Drive
Mesa, AZ 85205 U.S.A.
(602) 830-4540

Manufactured in the United States of America

ISBN 0-942548-49-3

Library of Congress Cataloging-in-Publication Data

TABLE OF CONTENTS

FRONT COVER: Eastern Aircraft FM-2 in front of Champlin Fighter Museum. *Dave Goss*
BACK COVER: A small sampling of the J. Curtis Earl gun collection. *Jay Miller/Aerofax, Inc.*

All photographs in the gun section are by Jim Thompson unless otherwise noted.

Champlin collection

Museum owner/director Doug Champlin.

ACKNOWLEDGEMENTS

I would like to take a moment to say thanks to the many people who contributed to the contents of this book:

Barrett Tillman, of Athena, Oregon, a noted aviation author, has been my long time friend and associate. Anytime I require text or research, Barrett is my source of choice.

Jim Thompson, of Mesa, Arizona, is both an aviation and a firearms buff (with a strong suit in automatic weapons). Jim researched and photographed most of the firearms section.

Jay Miller, of Arlington, Texas, is the owner of Aerofax, Inc., an aviation book publishing company, and in movie studio terminology, the producer of this volume. Jay and his staff tied together all the copy, research materials, and photography to make one manageable volume.

Jack Fellows and Roy Grinnell produced all the original art appearing in this book. I consider Jack and Roy the bright new stars of the booming aviation art community.

Lynda Geiser has been my personal secretary as well as the Museum office manager for the past five years. With all her other administrative duties, she still has found time to type, and in many cases, to retype pages of research and documentation for this book. She's done it all with a great sense of humor and has learned to be tolerant of authors, aviators, and collectors—since they are all a little crazy.

To all five men and one woman, I am extremely grateful.

Douglas L. Champlin

Doug Champlin

J. Curtis Earl (l.) and Doug Champlin with MG08/15.

—— A NOTE FROM DOUG CHAMPLIN...

"How did you get into this, Doug", is still the question I hear most often after nearly a quarter-century of collecting and restoring vintage military aircraft. I've reflected on this with some regularity over the years and have concluded that my interest can be traced back to the first few pieces of what became a considerable toy soldier collection. Given me by my parents, these meticulously sculpted figures still can be seen marching in column formation across the window sills of my Mesa, Arizona Falcon Field office.

My most significant early memory of firearm collecting is the result of a trip, some forty years ago, to Claremore, Oklahoma with my mother and older sister, Joanna. Joanna, who as an adult would become one of my most dedicated and vociferous supporters, had been invited to attend a dance at the Oklahoma Military Academy. Upon arrival in Claremore, we settled into a room at a small, but pleasant hotel owned by a Mr. Davis—who turned out to be a serious and accomplished gun collector.

Mr. Davis must have seen the collector's light in my young eyes when he saw me playing with the soldiers—for he was quick to pull me from the boredom of our room and give me a private showing of some of the special "toys" in his own collection. I was most impressed by his Old West

and Civil War era weapons as I had read books about the latter, and my grandmother, who had witnessed the early Cherokee Strip days in what then was known simply as the Oklahoma Territory, had spent hours telling me about the former.

Growing-up with this rich Oklahoma heritage certainly gave me the impetus to collect the very guns the pioneers had carried while hunting or doing battle. Because of this, Mr. Davis not only found me interested and willing but also extraordinarily enthusiastic. Most importantly I needed little encouragement.

Mr. Davis, as it turned out, was the solution to my parent's dilemma over birthday, Christmas, and special-occasion gifts. He often would be called upon to furnish select guns for my small, but rapidly growing collection. I well remember, for instance, the Christmas I was given a Civil War-era Navy Colt that had been acquired through Mr. Davis's efforts; it remains a treasured possession to this very day. Mr. Davis, unfortunately, died several years ago, but the legacy of his enthusiasm still can be found in my strong penchant for guns, and collecting in general.[1]

[1] Interestingly, part of the Davis collection today can be seen displayed in a state-owned museum in eastern Oklahoma.

Though my enthusiasm for gun collecting never waned, by the time I turned 14, my interests had become somewhat more eclectic, and like those of my father, had come to encompass motorcycles, other motor sports, and flying. The automobile hardware varied from Ford Model A's—costing all of $75—to more desirable foreign grand touring types. Eventually I focused on the more exotic sports cars and European-style road racing, and it was this segment of the sport that I continued to pursue with great vigor. By the time I was ready for college, I was completely enamored with automobile racing and had decided that I was going to make it my profession, if I possibly could.

My enthusiasm for competing with automobiles was tempered considerably during four years at the University of California at Berkeley and a two-year stint with the U.S. Army in Germany. Following my return to the states and my military discharge, however, my father, Joe, approved a conditional return to the racetrack—with the understanding that I be permitted to race cars for two years only. Once that stint was over, I would be obligated to return to the family oil and gas business.

The "two years" lasted almost seven—due at least in part to dad's own love of the sport and his empathy for my enthusiasm. In the interim,

I developed a close, and as it turned out, life-long friendship with Fred Carrillo (the manufacturer of the best racing-rods in the world), a close friend of my father. Through Fred, I grew to know the California racing scene with some intimacy and later was able to expand my racing horizons beyond those of state and regional contests. Fred and I eventually became partners in several Formula and Indy race car projects and later were fortunate to meet with some success in both.

Through the course of my automobile racing days, I had a sometimes quiet, sometimes vocal supporter who always provided sustenance when I needed it most—my brother, Bud. Being an engineer, a licensed pilot, and a graduate of the Massachusetts Institute of Technology, he was really the one perhaps most suited to an intimate involvement with race cars—but the fates ruled otherwise. Our family business and his personal family responsibilities prevented any behind-the-wheel participation. Regardless, he was there always to defend me against some irate race official or another driver, and perhaps most importantly, he kept Fred and me out of difficulty in the world of Indy car circuit high finance.

My mother, Jane, was neither a race car fan nor an aviation enthusiast. During my younger days, she managed to attend every little league game I played in, but later she conscientiously avoided patronizing my auto racing interests. Her attitude was summed up unceremoniously by her statement, "Motorcycles, race cars, and airplanes are all toys of the devil to make mothers and wives worry!" Her objections were openly displayed on many occasions, but she never was strident or shrill.

Unfortunately, my father never saw my car run at Indy. His death during 1970 came somewhat suddenly, but not before he managed to divert my interest in part from auto racing to aviation. Out of some deference to my mother, he apparently had concluded that if he could get me interested in aviation and flying, I might find the company airplane a somewhat safer and more gratifying means of high-speed transportation.

Somewhat to my father's chagrin, though the aviation seed had been sewn, it bore fruit in the form of an interest in vintage biplanes rather than the family business' sleek multi-engine corporate transports. Consequent to this, I met a local, soft-spoken, self-taught Oklahoma-farm-bred pilot who soon would become my mentor and best friend. Dwain Trenton was a consummate pilot with an evangelical zeal for flying that, to this day, I never have seen in any other aviator. He eventually upgraded my marginal Champion *Citabria*-level piloting skills to those of a proficient warbird pilot by stuffing me into a variety of ever-more-challenging aircraft including a Waco UPF-7 primary trainer, a North American SNJ *Texan* advanced trainer, a Douglas SBD *Dauntless* dive bomber, and finally, a hefty Grumman F6F *Hellcat* fighter.

From 1972 through 1978, Dwaine largely was responsible for the success of the Great Lakes biplane revival in which I was a participant. This activity, unfortunately, was cut short when he was killed test-flying a turboprop ag aircraft that then was being run through a Federal Aviation Administration certification program.

With Dwain gone and the inflationary clouds of the late 1970s looming on the horizon, the Great Lakes company was sold. Dwain was not forgotten, however, and when my first-born daughter, Christa arrived, Dwain became her middle name.

Although I didn't realize it at the time, Dwain's death marked a turning point in my piloting career. My interest in actually flying the fighters I was collecting was on the decline, and without actually realizing why it was happening, I found myself looking at the collection more and more as an historical artifact rather than a flying museum.

This reassessment, in retrospect, probably was due not only to the trauma of Dwain's passing, but also to my college background with its heavy emphasis on modern and European

history; it was natural for me to feel excitement for the events of World War II through the fighters—as this was as close as one was going to get to the Battle of Britain, Guadalcanal, or the Battle of Germany.

Through another friend and business associate, Joe DeFiore, I began to develop a strong interest in World War I aircraft. Fighter aviation, as I began to understand with Joe's help, did not begin during 1941, but rather during 1914 and the beginning of World War I.

The aircraft collection, during this period of redirection, continued to grow. The hangars I had built to accommodate it at the airport near Enid, Oklahoma, now were inadequate, and it was apparent that for further expansion to take place, I would have to move the aircraft to a location that would permit increased tourist accessibility and financial self-sufficiency. By now, I was aware that my hobby had become a business; most importantly, I was loving every minute of it.

Through a series of aircraft trades with the U.S. Marine Corps, I became acquainted with a retired Navy officer who fast became my good friend and eventually the person mainly responsible for the birth and success of the Mesa museum. Jim Fausz shared my love for fighter planes and air combat—and when the Mesa, Arizona city fathers learned of our interest in moving our fighter collection to their Falcon Field airport, Jim was retained to handle negotiations and firm up plans and requirements. The city quickly volunteered two original World War II hangars that, until then, had provided minimal utility, and once an agreement was reached, we began our move.

Jim became director of the museum during 1979, and with the help of such talented staff members as John Lane, Darlene Fleischhauer, Burl Teague, Lynda Geiser, Dave Goss, Charlie Hyer, Ken Tomb, J. R. Hostetler, Curt Smith, Wes Winter, and Laurie Pennell, to name a few, began the arduous task of creating a serious museum from a potpourri of full-scale aircraft, miscellaneous parts and pieces, and a hodge-podge of assorted memorabilia. I attribute the museum's successes to the policies of his management.[2]

During 1982 I came to realize that one of the responsibilities of a museum such as ours not only was to restore and preserve hardware, but also to preserve and disseminate the visual, oral, and written history of air combat. Accordingly, during 1982, Barrett Tillman, a noted aviation author with excellent aviation history and air combat writing credentials, was hired to accommodate the needs of our publishing operation. Barret's work eventually bore fruit in the form

of a number of significant historical references—and an on-going publishing program that continues to this very day.

Undoubtedly, one of the major events of the Museum's short history has been the decision of the American Fighter Aces Association to make the Museum its national headquarters. The Association elected to move to our facility during 1983, and the marriage has been a good one. The AFAA has brought considerable prestige to our collection as its members represent the essense of what the hardware is all about. Later in this publication you will be able to read more about the AFAA and its objectives.

As noted earlier, my interest in guns did not disappear with the arrival of racing cars and airplanes. In fact, during the course of developing the aircraft display, I also owned and operated a sporting arms manufacturing company. Returning to these gun roots during 1987, I called upon an old friend of some 15 years, J. Curtis Earl, owner of what many authorities then considered the finest machine gun collection in the world in private hands.

By 1987, J. Curtis had begun to look favorably upon the idea of spending more time fishing and hunting, and as a result, we began to discuss the idea of the Champlin Fighter Museum taking over his superb collection. After a brief period of negotiation, a sale price was reached and shortly afterwards, the J. Curtis Earl guns were on their way to our Mesa facility. We now maintain and display the collection in a 3,500 square foot vault which is integral with the rest of the museum.

Many have asked if the guns are appropriate for an aviation museum with a fighter theme. I feel they are. Again, seeing our *Spitfire* and Me 109 will probably be the closest most visitors ever will get to the Battle of Britain; similarly, seeing the Maxim, Vickers and Nambu guns is the closest many visitors ever will get to Verdun, the Somme, and the "Bloody Ridge" of Guadalcanal—all locations of battles involving the use of both aircraft and machine guns.

Since opening during 1981, museum attendance has grown from 20,000 to over 50,000 during 1988. Accordingly, I feel confident the collection will continue to increase in popularity. Additional displays and hangars presently are being planned, and with the help of the American Fighter Aces Association and the newly-formed Friends of the Aces program, the museum's future looks exceptionally bright.

Alas, the aces and I know we are mortal. Because of this, we would like to see the museum granted a more permanent status as a living tribute to fighters, fighter pilots, and fighter aviation. However, until that day arrives, we continue to enjoy the comradeship and knowledge we share with each other through the

aircraft—a knowledge in the form of a special heritage which never again will be duplicated in the history of aviation.

Douglas L. Champlin[3]
Mesa, Arizona
November 15, 1989

---

[2] Jim since has moved on to start another aviation museum, this time in Texas (The Lone Star Flight Museum).

[3] Douglas Champlin lives in Mesa, Arizona with his wife Laurel and shares custody of his two daughters, Christa and Claire. Business interests other than the Museum include oil and gas exploration, Arizona real estate, and resorts. His wife and daughters show quarter horses nationwide and enjoy skiing, boating, and fishing at their Lake Tahoe home.

J. Chester's dueling eagles are carved from one piece of wood.

A BRIEF HISTORY

In a world that today seems almost bursting with an ever increasing number of public and private aircraft and aviation collections, the Champlin Fighter Museum stands alone. It is the only facility of its type dedicated specifically to one category of aircraft and one genre of flying—fighters and air combat—and it is one of the very few maintaining all of its aircraft in flyable condition.

Perhaps as importantly, it represents, too, the realization of one man's long-standing desire to assemble, in one place, select and historically significant specimens of the world's most heralded combat weapons—the relatively small, heavily armed, highly maneuverable aircraft that have for the past three-quarters of a century, dominated not only the kingdom of air combat, but also the upper echelons of science, technology, and the many interrelated disciplines of dog-fighting and air-superiority.

As noted in Doug's short autobiographical sketch, the Champlin Fighter Museum was the result of an unbridled enthusiasm for collecting toy soldiers and guns. Over a period spanning

some three decades, this fetish spun off peripheral interests that included aircraft and flying, and with the encouragement of friends and relatives, it reached its zenith with the acquisition of a rare World War II-vintage North American P-51D *Mustang*.

Unfortunately, the mighty *Mustang's* tenure proved short-lived. Doug's father failed to see the wisdom of investing in vintage aviation hardware that left little room for pilot error while flying at speeds in excess of 400 mph, and as Doug fondly recalls, the *Mustang* somewhat unexpectedly and with little fanfare, "disappeared one day."

As the fates would have it, loss of the *Mustang* only added fuel to Doug's Enid, Oklahoma prairie fire. During 1971, a rare Goodyear FG-1D *Corsair* and a General Motors FM-2 *Wildcat* were acquired, and though the former eventually was sold to make room for other aircraft, the latter stuck around long enough to lay claim to plank-owner status in the Museum that exists today.

During the following several years, while manufacturing guns and dabbling in the family

energy and real estate businesses, Doug continued to add to his warbird inventory. By 1974, the collection appeared to have become large enough and interesting enough to be made into a genuine museum, but in Oklahoma, essential ingredients such as buildings and access to support personnel continued to be difficult to find. In response to this, Doug now moved ahead with plans to build suitable hangars and associated support facilities at the city airport, and two large structures eventually resulted. These quickly proved suitable for housing virtually all of the hardware, and consequently provided suitable space for maintenance and support.

In the interim, the Museum's inventory continued to grow and Doug began to refine his view of its objectives and philosophies. Additionally, and perhaps as importantly, he began to realize that Enid, Oklahoma, was not the ideal location for a tourist-oriented business. Though his love for "Sooner-country" was unequivocal, pragmatism dictated that other sites be considered for future expansion.

Daytona, Florida, home of the famous Daytona

Speedway (which justifies the city's "City of Speed" nickname) and "Daytona 500" stock car race, at first appeared the best of the many sites then being considered. When confronted with the museum's relocation possibility, the Daytona city fathers assembled an enticing package that included a sizable museum site positioned immediately adjacent to the world-famous race track.

Unfortunaely, a large barrier—the climate—stood in the way. Daytona's coastal humidty was antithetical to the long-time preservation of vintage aircraft in every way—and to house all the hardware in year-round, air-conditioned enclosures was not economically or logistically in the cards. Sadly, the Daytona offer had to be rejected.

Wes Winter, a friend of Doug's and a Great Lakes biplane dealer with a home office at Falcon Field Airport in Mesa, Arizona (approximately ten miles east of Phoenix), was aware of Doug's on-going site search. He also was aware of two relatively unused World War II-vintage hangars on Falcon Field property.

The Museum display areas provide access to hundreds of photographs of aces and aircraft.

The Museum gift shop offers a large selection of unusual, high-quality aviation items.

Glass cases display original aces' memorabilia.

Much of the aces' memorabilia belongs to the AFAA.

The AFAA collection describes U.S. and foreign aces.

Discussions with the airport manager verified the structures as museum candidates, and shortly afterwards, Doug made what proved to be a very convincing sales pitch to the Mesa city council.

By early-1980, the city fathers had become sold on the idea that Doug's museum should be located at Falcon Field. To underscore the sincerity of their commitment, $250,000 was set aside for the restoration and cosmetic improvement of the airport's two historically-significant hangars. As it were, these structures, built during 1941 to accommodate secret RAF training requirements prior to formal U.S. involvement in World War II, were ideally suited to meet the proposed Museum's space needs. Though nearly fifty years old, they were strong, environmentally acceptable, and ideally located in a dry climate. Because there were two identical structures, it also was possible to divide the Museum's collection into two logical groupings: one hangar would contain all the World War I-vintage aircraft, and the other would contain all the aircraft from World War II to the present.

Once a firm commitment from the Mesa city council and Falcon Field managers had been received, Doug made preparations to transfer the collection from Enid. During September of 1980, the first group of five aircraft was moved, and over the following six months, the rest of the collection was relocated, along with other memorabilia and support equipment.

Relocating the aircraft, as Doug recalls, had its "moments": "The move from Enid to Mesa was done in September of 1980. All but the German and World War I planes flew in. Jim Fausz had a mechnical failure in the *Spitfire* and ground looped it in Amarillo. The resulting dam-

age was severe enough to require a total rebuild.

"Ron Pucket (who placed second in the 1949 Cleveland Air Races in an F2G) ferried our F2G to Mesa (Ron later retired as an FAA test pilot in Wichita); Wes Winter ferried the FM-2; Jim Fausz ferried the F6F; and Dave Forrest ferried the FG-1D—all from Enid. Bill Yoak flew the P-40 over from California. Somehow they all arrived at Falcon Field at the same time. When they got there, Jim reported the F6F's engine was running roughly, and Bill reported the P-40's engine was overheating and he just wanted to get it on the ground. Making matters no less difficult was the fact we had no functioning control tower! It was a hectic arrival; Ron eventually ran off the active in the F2G following landing, while the other fighters were passing each other in 180° differential patterns overhead. It was lots of fun!"

On January 9, 1981, Doug's 40th birthday, the Champlin Fighter Museum opened its Falcon Field doors to the public for the first time. "Many of my out-of-state friends and supporters came to share my dream that day," Doug recalls, "but unfortunately, the happiness of the moment was shattered when I heard that Jim Benson of Enid, my good friend and business associate, had been killed that afternoon in a flying accident. Jim had flown an SNJ out to Mesa several weeks before. That was our last face-to-face visit. It was a tragic loss and a terrible end to what had been a terrific opening day."

Over the following several months, the Museum's tourist and visitor traffic quickly vindicated the city's support; by early spring it had become one of the area's most popular attractions. On April 26, the first of a select few flight demonstrations using Museum aircraft was

On rare, special occasions the entire Champlin fighter collection has been moved outdoors for display and photography purposes.

The "Hellcat" and "Wildcat" during early museum days in Enid, Oklahoma.

The "Spitfire" in Enid and prior to conversion to single-seat configuration.

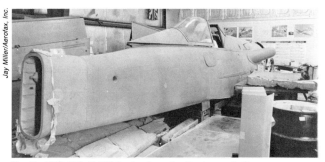

The Fw 190D-13 in Enid following its restoration tenure in Germany.

The Museum's maintenance/restoration shop and equipment.

Final Fw 190D-13 restoration efforts were undertaken in Mesa.

Sad condition of ''Spitfire'' following 1980 ground-loop in Amarillo, Texas during delivery flight from Enid to Mesa.

Fw 190D-13's Junkers-Jumo during restoration.

Museum's Messerschmitt began life as a Hispano HA.1112, #714112.

Gunther Rall, Adolf Galland, Randy Cunningham, and Walther Krupinski.

George Vaughn, Doug Campbell, and Ray Brooks with Doug Champlin.

undertaken when the Curtiss P-40E *Warhawk* and the Sopwith *Camel* were flown across the Falcon Field runways in front of a large crowd of visitors and Museum supporters. This fly-by practice was continued sporadically for select reunion groups and specialty dinner events until 1986, but after that, it was discontinued; Doug notes, ''The limited amount of flight time we logged plus the high cost of liability insurance made it prohibitive to keep the aircraft licensed. We continued, however, to restore our aircraft to complete airworthiness—and that practice is maintained to this very day.''

Doug's interest in guns had not lain dormant during the growth of his fighter collection and the move to Mesa. Though the machine guns did not have the massive tourist-drawing power of the fighters, they remained, for Doug, an item of strong personal interest. As a result, many significant additions were made during this period, even though the aircraft were getting all the attention.

With the acquisition of the J. Curtis Earl Collection, Doug's dual aircraft/machine gun interests effectively were merged when the guns arrived for display in the new museum. This

event proved fortunate, indeed, as it became apparent that the gun collection was a natural aircraft adjunct; in a sizable percentage of the fighter displays, for instance, machine guns, in one form or another, were a significant part of, if not the total of the aircraft's offensive or defensive weapons complement.

The Champlin Fighter Museum as it exists today did not reach fruition without the significant efforts and the contributions of many individuals. Doug's many friends (and relatives) unquestionably were instrumental in seeing it brought to reality, and Doug is the first to

acknowledge their support. From time and material donations, to simple morale, these unheralded volunteers have become the lifeblood of the museum's activity. Much of what visitors see in today's displays are the end product of work done by these silent team members.

As a symbol of appreciation to those who have contributed, the Museum is proud to emphasize that it serves to preserve and document not only artifacts and history, but also the memories of the men and women who made, and continue to make it all happen. Every single display item, from the tangled fighting eagles of hand carved

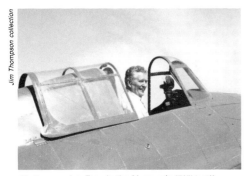

Marine ace Joe Foss in the Museum's "Wildcat".

Colonel Sid Woods in P-38 at the Museum.

"Douglas Campbell Becomes an Ace" by Roy Grinnell.

wood in the main display gallery, to the artwork, medals, machine guns, and aircraft found neatly arranged throughout the Museum's several enclosed display areas, represents an attempt to preserve at least in part, a small fragment of a heritage unique in the annals of world combat history.

Those of us at the Champlin Fighter Museum most sincerely hope that our efforts prove worthy of your support and interest.

A small part of the American automatic and machine gun collection displayed in one of many glass cases.

Special glass-enclosed vaults house the many guns displayed in the Museum's unique and extensive collection.

"Tiger Over China—1942" by Roy Grinnell, illustrates P-40s of Flying Tigers Dick Rossi, and Jim Cross.

THE CHAMPLIN FIGHTER MUSEUM
HOME OF THE ACES

By custom dating from France in 1915, a military aviator who downs five or more enemy aircraft in aerial combat qualifies as an "ace". For seven decades there has been no more glamourous title in the profession of arms. From World War I through the war in Vietnam, a little over 1,400 Americans—roughly one percent of all U.S. fighter pilots in that period—have qualified for the honored niche of acedom.

In 1960, seventy-five American fighter aces from World War II and the Korean War gathered in San Francisco to form the American Fighter Aces Association. Membership grew from the 60 founding members under the first president, Col. Jack Bradley, to today's membership of over 600 (some 85% of the surviving aces of World War I through Vietnam).

In its fledgling years AFAA struggled not only to organize, but to identify those qualified for membership. It was no easy task, for records were often contradictory or incomplete. By 1982, however, the organization was on solid footing and sought permanent quarters—an aerie, if you will, which its members could call their spiritual home.

At this point, Doug Champlin offered the Association the opportunity to make the Champlin Fighter Museum their permanent headquarters. It was a logical proposal—the world's only fighter museum joined by America's greatest fighter pilots. With the approval of the general membership, the Champlin Fighter Museum became the "Home of the American Fighter Aces" in 1983.

Moving into their new headquarters, the Association officers put out the call for items to display in the museum. Personal memorabilia poured in at unexpected rates as aces unloaded old footlockers or cruise boxes and even dismantled "I-love-me" rooms. A very successful fund-raising effort brought forth 40 glass display cases to exhibit the Aces' uniforms, flight gear, photos and documents.

A Gallery of Aces was established, and enlarged copies of photos and biographical sketches of the Aces, initially prepared by AFAA historian William N. Hess begn to adorn the hangar walls. The original collection of 300 has grown to over 600 photo/bios, with more being added periodically.

In the "hardware" arena, the American Fighter Aces have augmented the Fighter Museum's collection of 25 World War I and II aircraft with three jets—a Korean War F-86 and Vietnam-era F-4N, loaned by the U.S.A.F. and U.S. Navy respectively, and a Soviet MiG-17 given to the Aces by the government of Morocco.

Beyond the preservation of uniforms and documents, the Association's goal is to maintain a central repository of data on the 1400-plus American fighter aces since World War I for future historians. A section of the Champlin Fighter Museum's archive building has been provided for this purpose, and the Association now has information on over 800 aces, including many audio and/or videotaped interviews.

In 1984, largely through the efforts of then-president Jack Purdy, the "Friends of the American Fighter Aces" was formed as a support arm of the Association. Open to non-ace fighter aviation enthusiasts, the group has grown to over 800 members. As the inexorable march of time continues to thin the ranks of the Aces, the Friends will continue to preserve their artifacts and heritage for future generations.

AMERICAN FIGHTER ACES
DONOR RECOGNITION

The AFAA acknowledges contributors via a large recognition board bearing inscribed donor name plaques.

Uniforms and headgear are popular display items.

Virtually all displays are authentic and original.

The AFAA has assembled most of the memorabilia seen in the main hangars' glass cases.

In the Gallery of the Aces, the hangar walls are lined with biographical sketches of American fighter aces.

Each displayed item is fully identified along with particulars relating to its owner and/or contributor.

Large collection of scale models illustrate "planes the aces flew".

Plaque commemorates Falcon Field's RAF training.

An original "Taube" prior to delivery to the German Air Force during WWI.

WORLD WAR I—WORLD WAR II FIGHTER PILOTS AND FIGHTERS
A BRIEF OVERVIEW

Two plaques are prominent as visitors enter the Champlin Fighter Museum's main doors. One quotes the famous author Ernest Hemmingway, and the other commemorates the memory of the Royal Air Force pilots who trained at the Museum's Falcon Field location during World War II. Between them, they eloquently state what the Museum is all about—simply an untainted blending of patriotism of the highest order, superlative piloting skills, and the raw aesthetics of sophisticated combat hardware. Whereas the RAF plaque serves to recall an event rarely documented in World War II history, the Hemmingway quote speaks pithily of men in crises and the intimacy between man and machine enjoyed in the ethereal world of clouds and sky:

"You love a lot of things if you live around them. But there isn't any woman and there isn't any horse, not any before nor any after, that is as lovely as a great airplane. And men who love them are faithful to them even though they leave them for others. Man has one virginity to lose in fighters, and if it is a lovely airplane he loses it to, there is where his heart will forever be."

As vague as Hemmingway's allusions may be to some, to the vast majority of fighter pilots they represent an encapsulated image of air combat

and flying in its most tangible form. Such words provide a rare glimpse into a decidedly private world—a world offering the stark contrasts of monumental beauty and virtually instantaneous death; a world that outside the confines of cockpits, oxygen masks, and flying suits was, and still is, terribly harsh indeed.

Those of us who are of a more plebian nature, rarely if ever are privileged to this extraordinary, multi-dimensional environment. Accordingly, the Champlin Fighter Museum serves as an open time capsule permitting an intimate look into over seventy-five years of fighter pilots and fighter aircraft without the esoteric concerns of bogies, g-suits, helmets, or electronic warfare.

During the period covered, which is not much more than an average human lifespan, advances in aircraft performance and design—spanning from sub-100 mph wood-and-fabric biplanes to all-metal thirty-five-ton flame-spewing darts capable of traveling at speeds *twice* that of a .45 cal. bullet—not only have become possible, but commonplace. It has been a spectacularly rapid development cycle for one of man's most complex and sophisticated instruments of war, and one not matched by any other man-made object in history.

Piloting aircraft, particularly fighters, has always born with it the aura of great bravado and

everlasting adoration. The popular movies *Top Gun* and *Firefox*, for instance, poured fuel on what at one time had been only a smoldering fire. Consequently they irrevocably enhanced the image of an already notorious breed.

In truth, flying fighters in air combat always has been a dangerous, and sometimes distinctly uncompromising profession. During World War I, for instance, the statistical lifespan of a fighter pilot was measured in days for the gifted, and hours for those with more conventional skills. Even with the advent of the parachute, survival statistics improved little; as it were, wearing this life-saving device was considered "unmanly"— and rare was the scout pilot who was willing to swallow a little pride to ensure that he would be available to fight again another day (even among those who capitulated to common sense there remained the concern over the effect a parachute's weight might have on aircraft performance). Such attitudes, coupled with the inevitably aggresive nature of the opposition and a general lack of dependable hardware, made the odds against survival great, indeed.

The tenuous nature of the wood and fabric aircraft structures of World War I had given way to all-metal monocoque structures of extraordinary lightness and strength by the mid-1930s. Such improvements, arising from research

undertaken by both government and private enterprise, by 1939 had led to the rapid expansion of performance envelopes from World War I speeds of just over 100 mph and altitudes of just over 20,000 ft. to speeds of over 400 mph and altitudes of over 50,000 ft., respectively. By the time Hitler had begun his ill-fated march westward across Europe and eastward across Russia, virtually all the world's most advanced fighters were all-metal and capable of level flight speeds in excess of 300 mph.

World War II and the afore-mentioned improved technology upped the survivability odds, especially for Allied pilots, but consequently increased hardware complexity. For the first time, altitude capabilities had reached a point where cockpit environmental control was a crucial design consideration, and speeds had reached a point (the "transonic barrier") beyond which, for the time being, it was impossible to go faster. Though aircraft were considerably more dependable by the early 1940s, the enemy was no less aggressive, and death no less sudden and omnipresent.

Air-to-air combat during both world wars had proved decidedly effective as a means of eliminating enemy aircraft. All the basic ingredients for effective scout/pursuit/fighter designs had existed prior to the opening air-to-air skir-

The German ace Werner Voss and the noted aircraft builder Anthony Fokker observing a test flight.

Jules Vedrines in a 1914 Morane monoplane with a forward firing gun. Note bullet deflector on propeller.

Fokker's "Eindecker" had a synchronized forward-firing machine gun.

Noted German WWI ace Max Immelmann.

Nieuport 27 French pursuit at an aerodrome in France during WWI.

Albatros D.Va bearing striped markings of the "Oswald Boelcke" Jagdstaffel.

S.E.5A being utilized by American pilots following the end of WWI hostilities.

Sopwith "Pup" landing on HMS "Furious".

Snow-bound S.P.A.D. XIII with "Mayer III" printed under the cockpit combing. Markings were typical A.E.F.

Sopwith "Camel" suspended under dirigible, R.33.

An extraordinary line-up of Sopwith "Camels", probably in France during the latter stages of WWI.

Thomas Morse S-4 was an American-manufactured pursuit to compete with its European contemporaries.

mishes of World War I, but it took the actual onset of combat to bring them together as an integral unit. For instance, machine guns and aircraft existed prior to the war, and even had been tested for their respective compatibilities, but it wasn't until after the war's outbreak that the two were combined into a single-purpose machine optimized for the destruction of other aircraft and/or ground targets.

Following their integration, it still took the development of the synchronizer to permit forward firing of a machine gun through a propeller disk. The Germans were the first to utilize this device (August, 1915) in production aircraft (the Fokker *Eindecker*), and were followed, somewhat tardily, by the Allies several months later. Once the synchronizer became commonplace, however, the accuracy of *all* air-to-air weapons improved dramatically and the emphasis on dog-fighting (as air-to-air combat somewhat unceremoniously came to be called) shifted slightly from hardware to piloting technique.

It was the latter that gave rise to the legends of World War I aerial combat and created the aura of super-humanity surrounding the fighter pilot title. Such legendary aerial gladiators as Germany's Manfred von Richtofen and the U.S.'s Eddie Rickenbacker forever left their marks on the pages of aviation history during this cataclysmic period, and thousands of other pilots contributed to the mythical pool. Theirs was a skill that was all but unteachable in any classroom, and it came only with great daring and considerable natural ability. These prototypical aerial combatants were truly unique, and their like almost certainly will never again be seen in the skies of world conflict.

The mounts of these legendary pilots also achieved a stardom of their own. Among the most significant of the period were the Sopwith *Camel*, the Fokker D.VII, the Nieuport 17 and 27, the Fokker Dr.I *Dreidecker*, the Fokker *Eindecker*, the Sopwith *Pup*, the Pfalz D.XII, the S.E. 5, the Albatross D.I thru D.V, the S.P.A.D. VII and XIII, the Sopwith *Triplane*, and the Nieuport 28.

Additionally, World War I brought with it the first operational deployment of ships with aircraft aboard. These early navy excursions, utilizing either a catapult rail or a foredeck platform as the launch platform (some Sopwith *Camels*, however, were launched from towed barges), set precedent for later naval carriers, and proved the viability of operating aircraft from ocean-going platforms.

When the Great War ended with the armistice of November 1918, the majority of the world's air forces were almost instantaneously reduced to near skeletal inventory levels. In only one instance was an independent air service maintained, (an amalgamation of the Royal Flying Corps and Royal Naval Air Service had become the Royal Air Force on April 1, 1918), and even then it was kept on call only in consideration of the effectiveness of German Gotha bomber attacks on London during 1917.

Somewhat surprisingly, during the early 1930s the role of the fighter in air combat remained essentially undetermined. World War I had not left a firm vision of the type's usefulness, and with the world's economy in chaos, air forces found significant difficulty in convincing depression-era governments to provide fighter acquisition and research money.

Regardless of the economic situation, far-sighted visionaries working with aircraft companies scattered around the world continued their efforts to develop aircraft optimized for the air-to-air combat role. High-performance fighters were prototyped in seemingly endless variety, and as the years marching up to World War II passed, certain patterns began to emerge. The most obvious of these were a shift from biplane to monoplane configurations and a transition from wood and fabric to all-metal-monocoque

Boeing's P-26A was the most advanced monoplane readily available to the US military during the early 1930s.

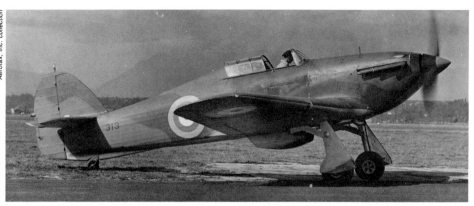

The Hawker ''Hurricane'' was perhaps the most important British fighter in the famous ''Battle of Britain''.

Bell ''Airacobra'' and ''Kingcobra'' production was undertaken at the company's Niagara Falls, New York facility.

The Focke Wulf FW 190 is considered by many authorities to be the finest German fighter of WWII.

France's most successful piston engine fighter of WWII was the Dewoitine D.520 (shown here in German markings).

Japan's quick and agile Mitsubishi ''Zero'' remains one of the most memorable fighters of its time.

Bell's P-59 "Airacomet" was the first US jet-propelled aircraft and the third jet aircraft in the world to fly.

Republic's F-84 "Thunderjet" was produced for the USAF in both straight wing and swept wing versions.

North American's F-86 "Sabrejet" has had a long operational life as a fighter. Its most recent use has been as an unmanned drone.

construction. Additionally, and perhaps as importantly, a mix of cannon and machine guns for armament packages was becoming more and more commonplace, and engines of a thousand or more horsepower were beginning to be a mandatory requirement.

By the mid-1930s, the rapid rise of Adolf Hitler and the ensuing threat of another world war began to build fires under the weapon industries of the various countries most directly affected. Germany already was beginning to place heavy emphasis on the design of advanced aircraft, and specific effort was being placed on creating fighters capable of speeds, altitudes, and maneuvering performance unmatched by any similar aircraft in the world. Britain, France, and Russia proved not far behind, and on the other side of the globe, the Japanese were setting precedent of their own.

The U.S., because of its geographic position, considered itself one of the least threatened of the directly involved countries and thus was significantly slower off the mark in putting money and manpower into advanced aircraft design. Nevertheless, independent work by farsighted and dedicated engineering teams was on-going, and it was this seminal effort that eventually would place the U.S. aircraft industry on the world fighter map.

Navy fighter development also now was reexamined with significant interest. By the mid--1930s, it had emerged from initial British experiments to become a sizable investment for several of the world's sea-going military powers—particularly and most notably the Japanese.

The most advanced Soviet fighter to see service during the Korean War was the MiG-15.

McDonnell's ubiquitous F-4 "Phantom II" was the most popular U.S. fighter produced after 1960.

Grumman's F-14A "Tomcat" (l.) and General Dynamics' F-16A "Fighting Falcon" are state-of-the-art US fighters.

McDonnell Douglas's F/A-18 "Hornet" is another state-of-the-art US fighter with exceptional performance.

The outbreak of the Spanish Civil War during 1936 was perhaps the first major skirmish since World War I to have a direct affect on fighter tactics. The Nationalists and the Republicans were both supplied hardware and personnel from a variety of sources, with the Germans blatantly supporting the former and the Allies tacitly supporting the latter. During the course of the war, tactics moved from the relatively disorganized free-for-all operations of World War I, to the German-developed *Rotte* two plane element (two *Rotten* made a *Schwarm*—in which each pair protected the other against an attack).

The development of these and other German tactics during the Spanish Civil War spread a different light on the subject of air combat, and most of the world's air forces privileged to the information were quick to take it to heart. Fighters now were given new roles and new emphasis, and discipline became the by-word of air-to-air tactics. Miscellaneous skirmishes involving the Japanese, Chinese, Germans, and other Axis forces permitted an experience base to be generated that shortly would be applied in principal to the opening battles of World War II.

U.S. involvement was declared formally following the Japanese attack on Pearl Harbor on December 7, 1941, and within days of the event, the War Department had come to realize that U.S. fighter technology and inventories were sadly lacking. Both the Germans and Japanese could lay claim to exceptional fighter hardware in the Messerschmitt Bf-109 and Mitsubishi *Zero-sen* series, respectively, and the British

already were well along in developing the early Supermarine *Spitfire* models.

During the nearly six years of war that followed, Allied and Axis fighter development resulted in unprecedented advances in technology, performance, and hardware. Many of the world's most famous and decidedly most successful fighter designs either reached maturity during this period or were its end product. Included were the North American P-51 *Mustang*, the Republic P-47 *Thunderbolt*, the Lockheed P-39 *Lightning*, the Focke-Wulf Fw 190, the Curtiss P-40 *Warhawk*, the Bell P-39 *Airacobra*, the Messerschmitt Bf-109, the Mikoyan & Gurevich MiG-3, the Yakovlev Yak-9, the Hawker *Hurricane*, the Supermarine *Spitfire*, the Mitsubishi *Zero-sen*, the Grumman F4F *Wildcat*, the Grumman F6F *Hellcat*, the Vought F4U *Corsair*, the Kawanishi N1K2 *Shiden*, and the precedent-setting Messerschmitt Me 262 *Schwalbe*, to name just a few.

World War II's air war is too large and too complex an event to document on these pages, but in summary it can best be stated that it served to mold and solidify the concept of the fighter as we know it today. Additionally, and perhaps most importantly, it set precedent for fighter tactics and piloting technique, and generated a fraternity of aces and near aces that have served as a well-spring for future fighter pilots that now has lasted nearly five decades. Lessons learned during this conflict led to a totally new definition for the word fighter, and vindicated, at long last, the arguments of the fighter visionaries of the preceding three decades.

21

Champlin collection

The Focke Wulf Fw 190D-13 is perhaps the rarest fighter in the Museum's extensive collection.

A REVIEW OF INDIVIDUAL AIRCRAFT
A RETROSPECTIVE

Doug Champlin often is asked to give brief historical summaries describing the specific aircraft in his collection and how they were acquired. Each, of course, has a unique and oftentimes lengthy story behind it, and therefore it would be difficult, if not impossible to provide such information in the limited scope of this book. What follows, therefore, is a brief overview of stories pertaining to select museum aircraft:

Fw 190D-13

During 1974 I was privileged to spend an entire afternoon with the great Prof. Kurt Tank, designer of the Focke-Wulf Fw 190 and select other noteworthy German combat aircraft. Our meeting had been prearranged under the aegis of the restoration of our Focke-Wulf Fw 190D-13, which then was sitting in Art Williams' restoration shop in Augsburg, Germany. Several years later, while reflecting on this event, it became apparent to me that meeting such fighter world giants had played a key role in my decision to revise my collecting philosophies. From my original intent to restore and fly the aircraft, my scope and direction had turned toward the philosophy of preservation—not only of the aircraft, but also of the heritage and legacies of the men and women who designed and flew them. This policy formally was integrated into our program when the American Fighter Aces Association selected the Museum as their national headquarters during 1983.

It would, of course, be impossible to relate all

the fascinating stories that have come from the great and near-great fighter pilots who have been kind enough to pay our Museum a visit, but some of these encounters and experiences should be highlighted. Over the years, I've been asked many times which aircraft is my favorite. In consideration of the many physical and aesthetic elements involved, the question has not been an easy one for me to answer. Based on rarity, however, and somewhat on fate, I would have to say the Focke-Wulf Fw 190D-13 probably is my first choice.

During March of 1972, I saw an ad for the Fw 190 in *Trade-A-Plane* and shortly afterwards, purchased it sight unseen from a David Kyte of Santa Barbara, California. Following consummation of the sale agreement, the aircraft was transported by truck back to our Enid, Oklahoma facility and there placed in temporary storage while I attempted to find someone in the U.S. or Germany with the skill and knowledge required to properly restore it. The latter proved no easy task, as the Fw 190D-13 was a very esoteric aircraft and people who had worked on it during World War II were a scarce commodity. Compounding the difficulty was the fact that our specimen, the only extant example known in the world, had been ravaged and stripped by souvenir hunters.

Several months after acquiring the rare German fighter, I saw an ad in *Sport Aviation* offering Focke-Wulf parts for sale. This chance discovery eventually developed into a long-term

personal friendship with Art Williams, who then was retiring from the U.S. Army with the intent of setting up an aircraft restoration facility in Augsburg, Germany. Art's wife, Christa, had been born and raised in Germany, and Art had decided to set up shop there, partially as a result. Following service in Vietnam and his Army departure, Art passed through Oklahoma where a deal was struck to restore the ailing Focke-Wulf fighter. Never one to delay, Art packed the aircraft and prepared it for shipping on the spot, and shortly afterwards, the two were on their way to Germany.

The Focke-Wulf spent the following six years in Germany while undergoing restoration, first at Augsburg, and later at Art's new shop in Guenzburg. It was during this time that Christa Williams arranged for Prof. Tank to visit the restoration coincident with one of my several Augsburg visits.

Prof. Tank proved a delightful and affable man and unhesitatingly related many fascinating stories concerning the development of the aircraft. During the course of our lengthy conversation, he expressed concern over who was going to fly the Fw 190 following its restoration. With a twinkle in his eye he was quick to mention that he personally had logged some 3,000 hours in the air as pilot-in-command, and that at 83 years of age, he would be pleased to fly "his" aircraft once again, for me... Not knowing exactly how to respond to this generous offer, I nodded my head affirmatively and said that

having him fly the Fw 190 certainly would be an honor.

That evening we were invited back to Munich where Prof. and Frau Tank served cocktails. I thought this presented a golden opportunity to involve Frau Tank in my dilemma, as my experience at home often had demonstrated that the family women often had other and usually counter opinions to my own... I therefore casually broached the subject of Prof. Tank flying the Fw 190 with Frau Tank. Her response, which came forth without hesitation, caught me by surprise. "Oh good", she quickly responded, "that means that I can get some color movies of him flying the Focke-Wulf. Be sure to tell me when he is going to fly so I can bring my camera."

Unfortunately, we will never know how serious she was or whether she simply was being a thoughtful and considerate wife placating her husband's passion for flying. The restoration project, perhaps mercifully, outlived the aspirations of the great Prof. Tank.

Six years after the restoration effort began, the Fw 190 was returned to Oklahoma. In the interim, I had obtained color photographs of our specific aircraft in its original wartime livery while lying derelict as war booty in Atlanta, Georgia. From those photographs, it was possible to determine that our aircraft was an Fw 190D-13 assigned to the Second Group of the 26th (JG26) Fighter Wing. Because it was built during February of 1945, it was operational only for a

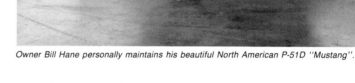

Supermarine "Spitfire" Mk.9T originally was delivered to Champlin as two-seat trainer.

Owner Bill Hane personally maintains his beautiful North American P-51D "Mustang".

short period before being captured intact by Canadian Forces in Flensburg, Germany. It was last flown in mock combat by Maj. Heinz Lange during June of 1945 against a Royal Air Force Hawker *Tempest*.

Col. Harold Watson, a noted "retriever" of Axis combat aircraft at the end of and immediately following World War II, participated in the recovery of our aircraft and three other "long-nose" Fw 190s from a German field near Flensburg. Upon recovery, all four were placed in temporary preservative and transported to the U.S. by ship.

After evaluation by the Air Force and various U.S. intelligence teams, our particular Focke-Wulf was given to the engineering department at Georgia Tech University. Over a period of time, it was heavily vandalized and eventually was hauled away by a retired Federal Aviation Administration employee. It lay in his back yard for several years and finally was bought by an Eastern Airlines pilot who then sold it to David Kyte. Years later, Kyte sold the aircraft to me.

Before plans for our move to Arizona were completed, Bud Briner, my associate in Enid, Oklahoma, painted the Fw 190 in authentic markings. An appropriate "JG 26" scheme was chosen and the aircraft was painted according-ly. In the interim, the Arizona move was consum-mated, so it was not until the aircraft arrived in Mesa that it finally was placed on display.

Restoration, never fully completed by Art Williams, was resumed by Champlin Fighter Museum maintenance director, Dave Goss and his staff, and the aircraft now is considered airworthy.

Messerschmitt Bf 109E

At my request, Art Williams spent considerable time looking all over Europe and the Middle East in an attempt to locate an original Messerschmitt Bf 109. No restorable examples were found and I therefore agreed that we should acquire a Spanish-built version (Hispano HA-1112) and convert it to original Bf 109 standard. An HA-1112 used in the movie *The Battle of Britain* then was located in Siegen, Germany and after it was bought, Williams hauled it back to Augsburg where it was placed in temporary storage. Coincident with the finding of the Hispano, Williams also was able to locate in Switzerland an original Bf 109E cowling and an associated Daimler-Benz DB 601 engine. These, too, were acquired, and eventually all were shipped to Augsburg. Restoration and modifica-tion of the aircraft to Bf 109E standard were undertaken there and took several years to com-plete. Eventually, the aircraft was painted in Maj. "Assi" Hahn's 1940-vintage markings and placed on display. During 1989, some fifteen years after the aircraft originally was acquired,

the engine was started and ground run for the first time.

Supermarine *Spitfire* Mk.9T

Another aircraft used during the filming of the movie *The Battle of Britain* is our Supermarine *Spitfire* Mk.9T. Originally an L.F. IX (RAF MJ772) and flown by Free French pilot Jacques Rem-linger of 341 Squadron, it was converted to its present configuration for use by the Irish Air Corps during 1950 at Supermarine's Southhampton facility. During 1966 it served as a camera ship during the filming of *The Battle of Britain*. Sir William Roberts added it to his famous Strathallan Collection in Scotland during 1970, and we purchased it from him during 1971.

On its ferry flight from Oklahoma to Arizona, Jim Fausz, then Museum director, had a mechanical failure and ground-looped the air-craft during roll-out following landing at the air-port in Amarillo, Texas. In light of the extensive repairs required following the accident, it was decided to completely restore the aircraft and consequently to cover over the second cockpit. After the restoration was completed, test pilot Steve Hinton flew it to a paint shop where it was painted in its original 341 Squadron markings (the blue spinner indicates its French heritage).

North American P-51D *Mustang*

The P-51 on display in our museum is owned

and maintained by my good friend, Bill Hane. Bill flies the aircraft almost weekly and also per-forms with it at airshows. While a member of the California Air National Guard, Bill vowed that someday he would fly a *Mustang* of his own. After several years as a successful Lake Tahoe realtor, he finally got his wish, and now devotes considerable time to demonstrating the aircraft and maintaining his business enterprises in Arizona and Nevada.

Republic P-47D *Thunderbolt*

According to our best research efforts, our P-47D is the oldest surviving *Thunderbolt*

Bf 109E cowling was found in Switzerland.

Aerofax, Inc. collection

Republic's P-47 "Thunderbolt" was built in both "razorback" (shown) and bubble canopy configurations.

Champlin collection

Museum's Republic P-47D is one of the very few surviving "razorbacks" and almost certainly the oldest.

specimen in the world. It was built during 1942 and was used throughout the war as a trainer. Sometime during the late 1950s, it was sold to the Bolivian Air Force. Later, the Bolivian government sold it to Jim Cullen of Westair International. Jim and I did some trading later, and the aircraft then was transported from La Paz, Bolivia to Carlsbad, California, where Dick Martin, over a period of five years, completely restored it.

The aircraft now is painted in the markings of Col. Robert Baseler who was commanding officer of the 325th *Checkertail* Fighter Group when they converted from Curtiss P-40s to P-47s while flying out of Foggia, Italy. Much to our delight, Col. Baseler was able to see his personal *Jug, Big Stud* fly again when we dedicated the

aircraft to him during 1981. We did not know at the time that he soon would succumb to cancer. His wife later told me that seeing the P-47 in his markings gave him a great lift in the last months of his most notable and distinguished life.

Lockheed P-38L *Lightning*

Our P-38 has a varied and remarkable history. Produced as a single-seat P-38L by Lockheed at their Burbank, California factory during 1944, it eventually was sent to Dallas for conversion to P-38M (two-seat, night-fighter) standard and thus became one of 77 such conversions completed. Never in combat, many years later it was sold by Dick Martin to a Latin American interest who used it to strafe the Dominican Republic Presidential Palace in an aborted coup attempt.

It wound-up being utilized by Batista's Cuban Air Force and ended its Latin American service in Honduras.

Eventually it was returned to the U.S. and Dick Martin, who then overhauled it for new owner Tom Friedkin. From Tom it went to Johnny Bolton (who later was killed in a P-51 accident) in Florida, and from Johnny to John Stokes of San Marcos, Texas. Cecil Harp and the late Bob Ellis of Stockton, California acquired it from John during 1978, and I bought it from them for our museum during 1983.

Because the Museum's policy is to preserve and display only aircraft that have achieved "ace" status (i.e., five aerial victories), a serious problem arose with the acquisition of the P-38M. During 1987, however, this problem was solved when a Texas P-38 owner made a decision to convert his aircraft into a two-seater. In short order we exchanged fairings and canopies and quickly returned our aircraft to its original P-38L (single-seat) configuration. We suppose this swap undoubtedly will confuse purest aviation historians and enthusiasts for years to come!

North American F-86F *Sabrejet*

The U.S. Air Force Museum has been kind enough to loan us a North American F-86F so that we might represent the pilots who made "ace" grade during the Korean War. My good friend and double Korean War ace, Gen. "Boots" Blesse, worked out the loan agreement between the American Fighter Aces Association, our museum, the U.S. Air Force Museum, and the South Korean Air Force (final operator of our aircraft).

Gen. Blesse attended the acceptance ceremony and received the aircraft on our behalf in South Korea, and the Oregon Air National

Guard then loaded the F-86F onto a Minnesota Air National Guard Lockheed C-130 *Hercules* for transport back to Mesa. An Army unit from the Arizona National Guard off-loaded the aircraft following its arrival. Somewhat surprisingly, all the coordination required between the various Guard units worked out very smoothly, and we came away from the experience with great admiration for the professionalism and dedication shown by the various personnel involved.

After removal of the South Korean Air Force markings from the aircraft, we repainted it in the markings of Gen. Blesse's Korean War-vintage aircraft. Today it is one of the more popular displays in our collection.

MiG-17 *Fresco*

Gen. "Boots" Blesse also was instrumental in our receiving, under the aegis of the American Fighter Aces Association, a rare MiG-17 for display purposes. This aircraft, from Morroco, was arranged through a meeting between Gen. Blesse and the Chief of Staff of the Royal Morrocan Air Force, Gen. Mohammed Kabbaj. As an ex-fighter pilot, Gen. Kabbaj was familiar with Gen. Blesse's Korean exploits and when asked to meet with him, graciously accepted. During a dinner in Morroco, an agreement concerning the MiG and how it was to be transported to the U.S. was reached. The Morrocans eventually flew the disassembled aircraft to Dover AFB in a transport and there helped off-load it onto a trailer manned by Champlin Fighter Museum staffers. From Dover, the aircraft was moved by truck to Mesa.

The MiG-17 in the Museum's collection is an early "A" model (no afterburner). It originally was delivered in Royal Morrocan Air Force markings. Apparently manufactured during 1955, it is in

Champlin collection

The MiG-17 remains one of the most outstanding jet-powered air combat aircraft of all time.

The MiG-17 (l.) and the F-86 meet on the ramp at the Museum.

Lockheed's P-38 "Lightning" had the attributes of speed and range, making it ideal for the Pacific Theatre.

Emphasis is placed on the maintenance and upkeep.

Museum aircraft retain authentic markings.

excellent condition and remains flyable. During 1990 it was decided to repaint the MiG in North Vietnamese markings to coincide with its adversarial relationship with our recently acquired F-4 *Phantom II*.

McDonnell F-4N *Phantom II*

Our F-4N is on long-term loan from the U.S. Navy. It has been restored in the 1968-vintage Vietnam-era markings of VF-21 from the U.S.S. *Ranger*. Depot personnel in San Diego did a magnificent job of painting the aircraft in memory of two crews who were lost during 1968 off the coast of Vietnam. Lieutenants Larry Lewis, Tony Miller, Jim Duensing, and Roy Haviland are memorialized by this aircraft.

Our aircraft originally was intended for display at the San Diego Aerospace Museum, but it was replaced by Vietnam Navy ace Randy Cunningham's aircraft. We were offered the F-4N thanks to the consideration of my good friend, Ed McKeller, director of the San Diego collection. When the aircraft became redundant, Ed called to work out details pertaining to its disassembly, transport, and reassembly. One of Ed's staff members, George Welsh, was instrumental in coordinating and overseeing the

McDonnell's ubiquitous F-4N "Phantom II" is the most advanced type currently on display at the Museum.

move. Walt Loftus, introduced to me by Herman Hamm and H.H. Ostroff of McDonnell (and both heavily involved in the original *Phantom II* pro-

duction and engineering programs) and his depot volunteers actually made the move possible through their generous assistance.

A S.P.A.D. XIII in WWI combat is depicted in this original work by highly talented and well-known aviation artist, Roy Grinnell. It is displayed in the Museum.

THE AIRCRAFT COLLECTION
WORLD WAR I

The photos and information in this section of the book pertain to the aircraft currently on display in the Champlin Fighter Museum. We have attempted also to integrate material relating to the gun systems carried by these aircraft wherever such items relate to our gun collection.

An original Albatros D.5 shortly before delivery to the German Air Force on the front during WWI.

SPECIFICATIONS:

MANUFACTURER: Albatros Flugzeug Werke
DESIGNATION: D.Va
FORMAL NAME: none
SERVICE/TYPE/NO. CREW: German Air Force fighter/single-seat
COUNTRY OF ORIGIN: Germany
SERVED FROM/TO: 1917 through 1918
LENGTH: 24 ft. 0-5/8 in.
WINGSPAN/WING AREA: 29 ft. 8¼ in./ 229 sq. ft.
HEIGHT: 8 ft. 10¼ in.
EMPTY WEIGHT: 1,511 lbs.

GROSS WEIGHT: 2,061 lbs.
MAX. SPEED: 103 mph
MAX. RANGE: 2 hour endurance
MAX. ALTITUDE: 20,500 ft.
ENGINE MANUFACTURER: Mercedes
ENGINE DESIGNATION: D.IIIa
ENGINE TYPE: six-cylinder inline water-cooled
POWER RATING: 180 hp
REGISTRATION/SERIAL NO.: NX36DV (reproduction)
NUMBER BUILT: approx. 2,000

ALBATROS D.Va

This German pursuit was developed during late 1916 and early 1917 in response to the improved Allied aircraft capabilities specifically represented by the S.E. 5 and S.P.A.D. Utilizing select components from the predecessor D.I/D.III series aircraft, the original D.V model, with its elliptical cross-section fuselage, proved only marginally superior to the aircraft it was designed to combat. Following field experience with the D.V, a number of minor modifications were introduced on the production line, these resulting in the D.Va. The most important physical change represented by this particular version was rerouting of the aileron cables through the lower wing.

A tendency for the lower wing to flutter and disintegrate during sustained dives from high altitude initially proved difficult to remedy. Structural testing of the aircraft produced no peculiarities, and it wasn't until a more detailed aerodynamic analysis was conducted that it was discovered the lower wing's single spar was positioned too far aft, thus permitting the flutter situation to develop. The fix that resulted, though only partially effective, was to attach a short auxiliary strut between the lower wing leading edge and the forward part of the vee-type interplane strut.

The D.V first entered German Air Force service during May of 1917. This model, along with the Albatros D.I/D.III series, became ubiquitous throughout the German Air Force inventory and remained among the most numerically significant German fighters of the war. Among the famous German pilots flying the Albatros fighters was Lt. von Hippel (one of the few pilots to survive a wing-failure of the type mentioned earlier), Lt. Hermann Goering, and the incomparable Manfred von Richthofen.

Armament for the D.V was typically a pair of fixed Spandau machine guns mounted above the forward fuselage and synchronized to fire through the propeller disk.

DOUG'S COMMENTS:

Whereas Williams Flugzeuge in Germany constructed the airframe and wings, Jim and Zona Appleby of Riverside, California finished this excellent full-scale replica and delivered it to Champlin in 1984. It was assembled for display, with its authentic engine, by CFM staff and the Applebys. The markings are of German ace, George van Hippel.

The Museum's Albatross D.Va cockpit.

The Museum's replica Albatros D.Va is painted in the markings of ''JagGeschwader 2'' and includes the original Mercedes engine.

Aviatik D.I in service during WWI. The type also was referred to as the Berg D.I in honor of its designer.

Aerofax, Inc. collection

SPECIFICATIONS:

MANUFACTURER: Desterreichische-
  Ungarische Flugzeugfabrik Aviatik
DESIGNATION: D.I
FORMAL NAME: Berg *Scout* (nickname)
SERVICE/TYPE/NO. CREW: Austro-
  Hungarian Air Force fighter/single-seat
COUNTRY OF ORIGIN: Austro-Hungary
SERVED FROM/TO: 1917 through 1918
LENGTH: 22 ft. 7 in.
WINGSPAN/WING AREA: 26 ft. 3 in./
  234.7 sq. ft. (approx.)
HEIGHT: 8 ft. 3 in.

EMPTY WEIGHT: 1,404 lbs.
GROSS WEIGHT: 1,906 lbs.
MAX. SPEED: 115.5 mph at sea level
MAX. RANGE: 1½ hour endurance
MAX. ALTITUDE: 20,000 ft.
ENGINE MANUFACTURER: Austro-Daimler
ENGINE DESIGNATION: none
ENGINE TYPE: six-cylinder in-line
  water-cooled
POWER RATING: 200 hp
REGISTRATION/SERIAL NO.: 101.40
NUMBER BUILT: approx. 750

AVIATIK D.I

The Aviatik D.I, known more commonly as the Berg D.I (after the last name of its designer, Julius von Berg) was the first indigenous Austro-Hungarian single-seat fighter to enter production. Several predecessor designs led up to the definitive D.I configuration, these including the Aviatik 30.14 of 1916, and the Aviatik 30.21. The latter, in fact, served as the series prototype and differed only in minor details from production D.Is.

Success of service trials led to the 30.21 being selected for production, and shortly afterwards, the Austro-Hungarian air force adopted it. Several other companies now were asked to participate in production, and specific production lots were assigned to Lohner, Thone & Fiala, M.A.G., and W.K.F.

Early production aircraft were powered by the 185 hp Austro-Daimler engine and later aircraft were powered by the 200 or 210 hp Austro-

The late Curt Smith applying the D.I's camouflage.

Champlin collection

Daimlers. Due to a lack of skilled labor, construction was kept as simple as possible; there was little unconventional about the D.I's mechanical design. The only item of note was its somewhat unconventional airfoil section (with reflex trailing edge). Basic construction materials consisted of mostly wood and fabric, with some steel tubing in select locations.

Because of its over-all simplicity, it was not a particularly difficult aircraft to fly or maintain. There were few complaints from D.I pilots excepting its propensity to overheat in the summer, its control sensitivity, and the chronic failures suffered by its gun synchronization system.

The D.I's armament complement varied, but basically consisted of one or two fixed Schwarzlose machine guns mounted just ahead of the cockpit and fitted with a synchronizing gear to enable them to fire forward through the propeller disk.

The museum's Aviatik was purchased by Art Williams in Europe, not as a World War I fighter, but as a salvage job which, at that time, mounted a vintage rotary engine which later proved beyond repair. For all intents and purposes, it seemed to be a club or school-manufactured instructional 2-seater, and must have looked vaguely like an early Sopwith. In the course of disassembling his prize, Williams found bits of a very strange finish, which he described as "zig-zaggy gray, lilac and brown". Digging further and applying some paint stripper, he found:

AV D.II
TH-FI 101-40

The 101-40 coding appeared in several other

places. Williams began a little backward detective work, uncovered former owners, and deciphered the meaning of the codes. He realized he had a trimmed-down Aviatik D.I built by Thone and Fiala (for production purposes, the 225 hp version with the largest radiator was usually called a D.II) which had been sliced like a potato and fitted with a crude but sturdy two-place top.

Even the date proofs were there: September 11, 1918. Williams recognized the thin, flexible wings designed to bend with Alpine updrafts.

Just as intriguing, this was Berg's own airplane, perhaps concealed from Truce Commission authorities or stashed as an asset for other reasons. Nothing of unit or pilot assignment could be found, but the airplane had been acquired from Berg's widow's estate.

The paint scheme was authenticated by Dr. Martin O'Connor, noted authority on the Austro-Hungarian Flying Service and author of the Champlin Fighter Museum Press volume *Air Aces of the Austro-Hungarian Empire*. The colors were copied and laid out in detail based upon the only existing original fabric from Italy's Leonardo deVinci Museum.

While almost all the original metal fittings for the aircraft were used in refurbishment, the wings and some of the structure required replacement, with reference to drawings made from the only other surviving Aviatik in the Vienna Technical Museum.

Champlin purchased the airplane in 1978, and completed the restoration in Arizona with a new radiator and refurbished, authentic Austro-Daimler engine. It is representative of the air-

craft flown by such Austro-Hungarian aces as Frank Linke-Crawford (twenty-seven victories), Julius Arigi (thirty-two), and Bela Macourek (five).

DOUG'S COMMENTS:

Perhaps most intriguing is the Austro-Hungarian Aviatik D.I, the only intact example of its type in the world. During 1975 it was

The Museum's Aviatik D.I cockpit.

Jay Miller/Aerofax, Inc.

located in Austria by my European contact, Art Williams, who advised me of its status. The designer, Julius von Berg, had stashed some D.Is for postwar use and his widow had kept the one Williams found. It had been heavily modified with a Gnome rotary instead of stationary engine and had a two-seat front cockpit. This aircraft was one of the first four ever used by Air Austria and as such may be the world's oldest surviving commercial aircraft.

That was the good news. The bad news: we had no engine. Only three Austro-Daimler 200-hp engines were known in the world, but after four years of negotiations I acquired one from the Air Force Museum. The research phase included a trip to the Vienna Technical Museum, which had a partial D.I, and the staff was most helpful in assisting us with detailed information.

Jay Miller/Aerofax, Inc.

The Museum's original Aviatik D.I is the rarest aircraft in the collection as there is only one other example known to be extant.

SPECIFICATIONS:

MANUFACTURER: Fokker Flugzeug Werke
DESIGNATION: D.VII
FORMAL NAME: none
SERVICE/TYPE/NO. CREW: German Air Force fighter/single-seat
COUNTRY OF ORIGIN: Germany
SERVED FROM/TO: 1918 through late 1920s
LENGTH: 22 ft. 11-5/8 in.
WINGSPAN/WING AREA: 29 ft. 3½ in./ 221.4 sq. ft.
HEIGHT: 9 ft. 2¼ in.
EMPTY WEIGHT: 1,540 lbs.

GROSS WEIGHT: 1,870 lbs.
MAX. SPEED: 116.6 mph at 3,280 ft.
MAX. RANGE: 1½ hour endurance
MAX. ALTITUDE: 19,600 ft.
ENGINE MANUFACTURER: Mercedes
ENGINE DESIGNATION: D.III
ENGINE TYPE: six-cylinder in-line water-cooled
POWER RATING: 160-200 hp
REGISTRATION/SERIAL NO.: N38038 (reproduction)
NUMBER BUILT: approx. 400

A captured Fokker D.VII being reviewed by US personnel shortly after the cessation of WWI hostilities.

FOKKER D.VII

The Fokker D.VII unquestionably is the most technologically significant production aircraft of German origin to come out of World War I. Created by the genius of Fokker's chief designer, Reinhold Platz—the same engineer who created the outstanding Fokker Dr.I triplane fighter—the D.VII was the scourge of the skies over Europe during the last year of the war.

The D.VII was the end product of what started as the Fokker VII prototype. This aircraft, following initial test flights, was entered in a German Air Force competition calling for a new "single-seat fighting scout". The fly-off resulted in the aircraft being declared the unanimous choice for production, and shortly afterwards, production facilities operated not only by Fokker, but also by Albatros, were producing the aircraft in ever-increasing quantities.

The D.VII used essentially the same construction techniques developed for the Dr.I, including a welded steel tube fuselage and all-wood wings. However, the latter, with the D.VII, were built-up around two box-type spars rather than a single laminated spar, and the wing section tapered toward the wing tips.

The first D.VIIs were powered either by a 160 hp Mercedes D.III or 185 hp B.M.W.III six-cylinder in-line water-cooled engine. This powerplant arrangement resulted in the aircraft having a somewhat unusual exposed, nose-mounted radiator, which had not previously been seen on production single-seat German pursuits.

When it first entered combat during the spring of 1918, the D.II quickly proved itself to be a docile, yet highly maneuverable mount. Pilots found it easy to fly, confidence-generating, and with specific control attributes that permitted select advantages when engaged in air-to-air combat (stalls were predictable and controllable).

The D.VII's successes, unfortunately for the Germans, proved too little, too late. Though few Allied aircraft could successfully compete with it one-on-one when in the hands of a competent pilot, the limited number of D.VIIs in service proved an overwhelming disadvantage. Even in consideration of this, the type's effectivity was such that it was the only aircraft, at the end of the war, specifically singled out for mention in the Armistice Agreement article designating war booty that was to be handed over to the Allies.

Following the cessation of hostilities during November of 1918, Fokker continued to produce a limited number of D.VII and D.VII derivatives for use by the Dutch Air Force and select civilian customers. The last of these was removed from service during the late 1920s, though sporadic individual examples were flown with some consistency into the early 1930s.

The standard armament package for most Fokker D.VIIs consisted of two fixed Spandau machine guns mounted ahead of the cockpit and synchronized to fire through the propeller disk.

DOUG'S COMMENTS:

The fuselage was welded up by Joe DeFiori, and we purchased it in bare-bones configuration. Wings, engine and accessories were added by Jim and Zona Appleby to complete the project. One of the most difficult aspects was re-printing the unique lozenge-pattern camouflage on fabric, over which we added the symbolic winged sword emblem of Capt. Rudolf Berthold, a 40-victory ace.

The Museum's Fokker D.VII cockpit.

The Museum's Fokker D.VII replica is an extremely accurate rendering of the original aircraft including the latter's six-cylinder Mercedes engine.

Aerofax, Inc. collection

Fokker D.VIII demonstrates the exceptional strength of its then-unusual high-wing monoplane configuration.

SPECIFICATIONS:

MANUFACTURER: Fokker Flugzeug-Werke
DESIGNATION: D.VIII
FORMAL NAME: none
SERVICE/TYPE/NO. CREW: German Air Force fighter/single-seat
COUNTRY OF ORIGIN: Germany
SERVED FROM/TO: 1918 through early 1920s
LENGTH: 19 ft. 2¾ in.
WINGSPAN/WING AREA: 27 ft. 4 3/8 in./ 115.5 sq. ft.
HEIGHT: 8 ft. 6 3/8 in.

EMPTY WEIGHT: 893 lbs.
GROSS WEIGHT: 1,334 lbs.
MAX. SPEED: 127.5 mph at sea level
MAX. RANGE: 1½ hour endurance
MAX. ALTITUDE: 19,680 ft.
ENGINE MANUFACTURER: Oberursel
ENGINE DESIGNATION: U.II
ENGINE TYPE: nine-cylinder air-cooled rotary
POWER RATING: 110 hp
REGISTRATION/SERIAL NO.: NX7557U (replica)
NUMBER BUILT: approx. 380

FOKKER D.VIII

The Fokker D.VIII evolved from the V26 parasol monoplane developed by the ever-capable Reinhold Platz. In response to a single-seat fighter competition held during early 1918, Platz and Fokker elected to enter the V26, in modified form. Following an analysis by test pilots and combat pilots, it proved superior to the considerable competition in take-off time, climb to altitude, and diving speed, and shortly afterwards, the German Air Force ordered it into production.

Unfortunately, immediately following entry into service during August of 1918, the E.V (as the D.VIII initially was called) suffered a number of difficulties, including a shortage of castor oil for engine lubrication, and a series of inexplicable wing failures. The latter eventually was traced to spar construction anomalies which were rectified quickly, thus permitting the aircraft to be reinstated in production.

Already-produced aircraft brought up to the new standard, as well as all new aircraft, now were referred to as D.VIIIs. Unfortunately for the type, by the time its problems were resolved, and by the time it entered frontline service, the war effectively had drawn to a close. At least one

noteworthy ace, however, Lt. Theo Osterkamp, is known to have flown the D.VIII in combat, and in fact scored his 25th and 26th aerial victories in it.

The standard armament package consisted of two fixed, synchronized Spandau machine guns mounted just ahead of the cockpit and firing forward through the propeller disk.

Only one authentic D.VIII exists, in the Caproni Museum in Italy. E.O. Swearingen of Worth, Illinois, visited that aircraft and corresponded with designer Reinhold Platz in preparation for building the Museum's aircraft in the 1960s. After much consultation and measurement, plans were drawn and work begun. A Warner radial was substituted for the old rotary in the interest of reliability and safety, since Swearingen flew the aircraft frequently.

Champlin purchased the aircraft from Swearingen in 1980.

Jay Miller/Aerofax, Inc.

The Museum's Fokker D.VIII cockpit.

Aerofax, Inc. collection

Fokker's D.VIII was prototyped as the Fokker E.V. The E.V helped sell the type to the German Air Force.

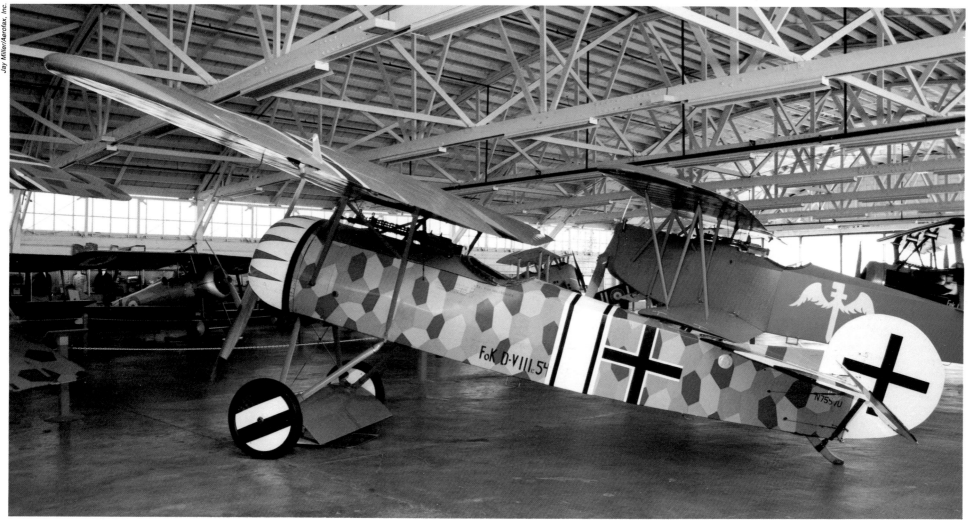

The Museum's replica Fokker D.VIII carries an authentic camouflage scheme and is powered by a conventional radial rather than an actual rotary engine.

German ace Werner Voss in his Fokker Dr.I triplane. Crew are walking the aircraft immediately prior to takeoff.

SPECIFICATIONS:

MANUFACTURER: Fokker Flugzeug Werke
DESIGNATION: Dr.I
FORMAL NAME: *Dreidecker* (three-wing)
SERVICE/TYPE/NO. CREW: German Air Force fighter/single-seat
COUNTRY OF ORIGIN: Germany
SERVED FROM/TO: 1917 through 1918
LENGTH: 18 ft. 11 1/8 in.
WINGSPAN/WING AREA: 23 ft. 7 3/8 in./ 201.5 sq. ft.
HEIGHT: 9 ft. 8 3/8 in.
EMPTY WEIGHT: 893.2 lbs.

GROSS WEIGHT: 1,289.2 lbs.
MAX. SPEED: 103.12 mph
MAX. RANGE: 1½ hour endurance
MAX. ALTITUDE: 19,600 ft.
ENGINE MANUFACTURER: Thulin-manufactured Le Rhone
ENGINE DESIGNATION: none
ENGINE TYPE: nine-cylinder air-cooled rotary
POWER RATING: 110 hp
REGISTRATION/SERIAL NO.: NX2203 (replica)
NUMBER BUILT: approx. 320

FOKKER Dr.I

The Fokker Dr.I *Dreidecker*, often referred to informally as the Fokker *Triplane*, was not, contrary to reputation, the first of the small triplane scouts utilized by the combatants during World War I. It was, in fact, developed by Fokker during the spring of 1917 in response to the successes then being enjoyed in the skies over Europe by the British Sopwith *Triplane*. German response to this aircraft was rapid and ubiquitous—a large number of triplane prototypes were built by the various German aircraft manufacturers and flown-off against each other during the course of several air force sponsored competitions.

The Fokker prototype, known as the V3 and generated by the incomparable engineering talent of Reinhold Platz, proved the best of the many competing designs and was ordered into production. The first three aircraft were rolled

The recovered remains of von Richthofen's Dr.I.

out as Fokker FIs, but this designation was dropped in favor of Dr.I with the fourth and all subsequent aircraft.

Design of the Dr.I, though typically Fokker, proved progressive for its day. Platz had optimized the aircraft for maneuverability, and in so doing, had created a wing configuration that provided sufficient wing area while reducing frontal area to a bare minimum. Construction difficulties also were minimized by keeping wing construction techniques, wing chords, and the airfoil sections all identical. The fuselage and tail surfaces were typically steel tube with fabric covering.

The Dr.I first entered German Air Force service during August of 1917. Many competent and well-known German pilots eventually used the Dr.I as their preferred combat mount. The most famous of these was the legendary Manfred von Richthofen, who first flew the *Dreidecker* during September of 1917. He was to remain a strong proponent of the type until his death in Dr.I #425/17 on April 21, 1918.

Other notable German pilots who flew the Dr.I included Werner Voss and Heinrich Gontermann. Voss eventually was killed while flying a Dr.I, though not before netting a total of 48 victories.

Poor quality control practices at Fokker led to the loss of several Dr.Is due to wing structural failure during the fall of 1917. It wasn't until near the end of the year that the problem was confronted and rectified. The type remained in service through the middle of 1918, but after the

completion of a relatively small number of aircraft, it was replaced on Fokker production lines by the more advanced and significantly more capable D.VII.

The standard armament package found on the Dr.I consisted of two fixed, synchronized Spandau machine guns mounted just ahead of the cockpit and firing forward through the propeller disk.

The last authentic Dr.I was destroyed in an Allied bombing raid on Berlin in World War II.

DOUG'S COMMENTS:

Dentist Richard Coughlin of New York began work on the Museum's aircraft in 1958, and completed it in 1972. His Warner Scarab failed on his initial flight, resulting in a crash. Champlin acquired the sleek black replica in 1978, and rebuilt it completely, including the engine. During 1990 the radial that had graced the cowling of the Dr.I was replaced with a rotary engine.

The Museum's Fokker Dr.I cockpit.

The Museum's Fokker Dr.1 replica originally was built and flown with a radial engine (seen here). During early 1990, however, an authentic rotary engine was installed.

Der neue Fokker-Eindecker
für Rückenflüge

Anthony Fokker is seen sitting in the cockpit of one of the original, gunless, "Eindeckers".

SPECIFICATIONS:

MANUFACTURER: Fokker Flugzeug Werke
DESIGNATION: E.III
FORMAL NAME: *Eindecker*
SERVICE/TYPE/NO. CREW: German Air Force fighter/single-seat
COUNTRY OF ORIGIN: Germany
SERVED FROM/TO: 1915 through 1916
LENGTH: 23 ft. 6½ in.
WINGSPAN/WING AREA: 31 ft. 2¾ in./ 172.8 sq. ft.
HEIGHT: 7 ft. 10½ in.
EMPTY WEIGHT: 878 lbs.

GROSS WEIGHT: 1,342 lbs.
MAX. SPEED: 87.5 mph
MAX. RANGE: 1½ hour endurance
MAX. ALTITUDE: 12,000 ft.
ENGINE MANUFACTURER: Oberursel
ENGINE DESIGNATION: U.I
ENGINE TYPE: nine-cylinder air-cooled rotary
POWER RATING: 100 hp
REGISTRATION/SERIAL NO.: N3363G (reproduction)
NUMBER BUILT: approx. 200

FOKKER E.III

The Fokker E.III, sometimes referred to as the *Eindecker* (one wing), deserves a significant place in the history of aerial combat not necessarily because of its prowess or its distinctive fighter attributes, but rather because it was the first production combat aircraft in the world to be equipped with a forward-firing, fixed machine gun synchronized to fire between the propeller blades.

The E.III, which was the primary production version of an extensive series of monoplanes generated by the Fokker company during the 1915/1916 period, was the most notable development of the E.I, an aircraft personally demonstrated by Anthony Fokker to the German Air Force and later flown, in production form, by German aces Oswald Boelcke and Max Immelmann.

Earlier Fokker monoplane configurations such as the M 5k (A.III), equipped with a machine gun firing through the propeller arch had served to convince a somewhat dubious German Air Force hierarchy that Fokker's innovative synchronizing gear actually worked. Though others also had developed viable synchronizers, it took Fokker's extraordinary skills as a salesman to convince German generals that such systems really functioned without permitting propeller damage.

The E.I had been followed into production by the modestly upgraded E.II with its stronger structure, and in turn, the E.II was followed by the ultimate *Eindecker* perturbation, the E.III. This latter version entered German Air Force service during September of 1915, and in short order began claiming allied victims with considerable alacrity. As it turned out, allied pilots were taken totally unawares by the E.III's forward firing machine gun arrangement, and thus were unprepared when the small German monoplane began an attack from the rear. During the latter half of 1915 through early 1916, the E.III scored numerous kills as a result of its small, but deadly technological advantage.

One sidelight to the history of the E.III harks back to Max Immelmann's use of the aircraft. Immelman, while flying *Eindeckers*, perfected the technique of diving out of the sun (if possible) during an attack, then pitching up into a follow-

through climb to what appeared to be the aircraft's stall speed, and then at just the right moment (as the aircraft neared vertical altitude),

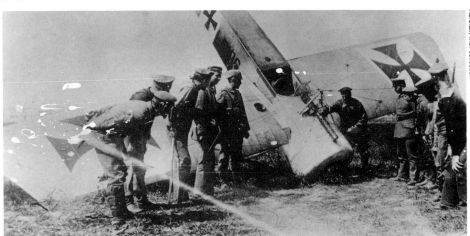

Observers appear to be expressing great interest in this crashed "Eindecker's" synchronized machine gun.

The Museum's Fokker "Eindecker" cockpit.

kicked-in enough rudder to make the aircraft reverse direction and thus be prepared for another attack without significant loss of altitude. Thus came into being the famous "Immelmann Turn"—often referred to simply as an Immelmann. Ironically, Immelmann lost his life in an E.III on June 18, 1916, when he was attacked and killed by Lt. G.R. McCubbin and his observer, J.H. Waller who were flying an F.E. 2b.

A further development of the *Eindecker* series eventually surfaced as the E.IV, but this aircraft, with its larger and more powerful engine, increased weaponry complement (two Spandau machine guns), and other additions proved far less agile than its predecessors and thus not suitable for aerial combat. Its tenure in the skies over Europe proved short-lived.

By 1916, the *Eindecker's* performance and prowess had been overshadowed by newer biplane and triplane designs on both sides of the war, and it soon was relegated to less vulnerable roles. By the end of 1916, few remained in service.

The standard armament package found on the *Eindecker* consisted of a single fixed, synchronized Spandau machine gun, offset to the starboard side of the forward cowling, firing through the propeller disk.

The Museum's *Eindecker* is probably the most authentic replica in the world. Unlike most replicas, this one features an original rotary engine.

DOUG'S COMMENTS:

As historians now acknowledge, the first production fighter aircraft was the Fokker E.III, a prewar design rendered lethal with addition of a machine gun synchronized to fire through the propeller. Jim and Zona Appleby were commissioned to produce a reproduction *Eindecker* in 1981, and the result was the authentic aircraft now on display. Today's jet jockies often are astonished to see a "flying tail" on a 1914 aircraft—the great-great-grandfather of their own F-15s and F-16s.

The Museum's "Eindecker" is considered one of the most authentic replicas of this aircraft in the world as it emulates the original in every respect.

Aerolax, Inc. collection

SPECIFICATIONS:

MANUFACTURER: Society Anonyme des
   Establissments Nieuport
DESIGNATION: 27
FORMAL NAME: none
SERVICE/TYPE/NO. CREW: Aviation Militaire
   fighter/single-seat
COUNTRY OF ORIGIN: France
SERVED FROM/TO: 1917 through 1918
LENGTH: 19 ft. 3½ in.
WINGSPAN/WING AREA: 26 ft. 10 in.
HEIGHT: 7 ft. 11½ in.
EMPTY WEIGHT: 782 lbs.

GROSS WEIGHT: 1,540 lbs.
MAX. SPEED: 128 mph
MAX. RANGE: 2 hour endurance
MAX. ALTITUDE: 18,200 ft.
ENGINE MANUFACTURER: Gnome-Rhone
ENGINE DESIGNATION: Monosoupape 9N
ENGINE TYPE: nine-cylinder air-cooled rotary
POWER RATING: 160 hp
REGISTRATION/SERIAL NO.: N5597M
   (replica)
NUMBER BUILT: approx. 1,000

A Nieuport 27 captured and test-flown by the German Air Force and bearing German markings.

NIEUPORT 27

Nieuport, by the advent of the Nieuport 27, had gained a considerable reputation among the Allied powers as the builder of exceptional pursuits. The Nieuport 11 and Nieuport 17, for instance, had generated excellent kill/loss ratios during the first few years of the war, and pilots found the aircraft to have few vices and many attributes.

The Nieuport 24, with its many refinements, a 130 hp Le Rhone rotary engine, and an internally sprung tail skid, had followed the 11 and 17, and in turn, had been replaced in production by the last of the Nieuport "vee-strutters" (nicknamed after the shape of the interplane struts between the wings), the Nieuport 27.

This pursuit was powered by the 120 hp Le Rhone rotary and had rounded wing tips, a curved-side fuselage, and tail surfaces similar to those found on its predecessor. It eventually served in limited numbers with the French air forces, and similarly was utilized by the British during a period lasting from the summer of 1917 through the following spring. Later, the Nieuport 27 was supplied to the Italians, who also built a significant number at their Nieuport-Macchi facility. Some 287 Nieuport 27s also were acquired by the U.S. for use as trainers in France.

In combat, the Nieuport 27 was found to offer little advantage over its predecessors. Additionally, its armament complement, consisting of a single synchronized Lewis or a single Vickers machine gun, was considered too light for the combat then taking place in the skies over Europe, and accordingly, its service career was short and relatively uneventful.

The Museum's specimen depicts a typical British-service Nieuport with a single overwing Lewis. It was built by expert replica constructors Carl Swanson and Jerry Thornhill in 1980. Brakes and a tiny tail wheel are concessions to safety. Champlin added the aircraft to his collection the year it was finished.

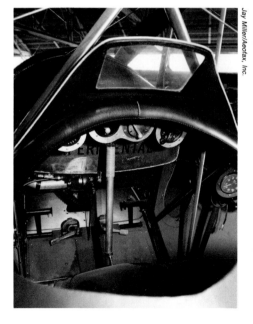

Jay Miller/Aeofax, Inc.

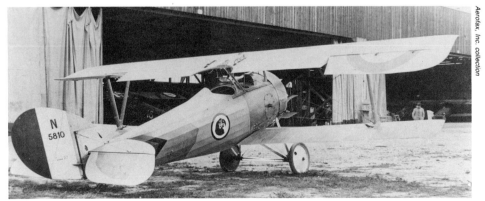

Aerofax, Inc. collection

An operational Nieuport 27 with guns removed from its upper wing. Rudder size was noteworthy.

The Museum's Nieuport 27 replica is equipped with a single over-wing Lewis machine gun and is painted unusually in British markings.

SPECIFICATIONS:

MANUFACTURER: Pfalz Flugzeug-Werke
DESIGNATION: D.XII
FORMAL NAME: none
SERVICE/TYPE/NO. CREW: German Air Force fighter/single-seat
COUNTRY OF ORIGIN: Germany
SERVED FROM/TO:1918
LENGTH:20 ft. 20 in.
WINGSPAN/WING AREA:29 ft. 6 3/8 in./ 126.2 sq. ft.
HEIGHT: 8 ft. 10¼ in.
EMPTY WEIGHT: 1,571 lbs.

GROSS WEIGHT: 1,973.4 lbs.
MAX. SPEED: 106.25 mph
MAX. RANGE: 2½ hour endurance
MAX. ALTITUDE: 18,500 ft.
ENGINE MANUFACTURER: Mercedes
ENGINE DESIGNATION: D.IIIa
ENGINE TYPE: six-cylinder in-line water-cooled
POWER RATING: 180 hp
REGISTRATION/SERIAL NO. N43C/3498
NUMBER BUILT unknown

A German Air Force Pfalz D.XII probably photographed in the US shortly after the cessation of WWI hostilities.

PFALZ D.XII

The Pfalz D.XII first was noted during special fighter trials held at Adlershof, Germany during June of 1918. Two versions of the aircraft were demonstrated, each powered by a different engine. At the end of the trials, both D.XIIs had performed admirably, and shortly afterwards, the German Air Force ordered the type into production, primarily to serve as a back-up to the highly competent Fokker D.VII.

Reaction to the D.XII when it began arriving at the front during September of 1918, was not particularly positive, but after several weeks of utilization, pilot attitudes began to change. In many respects the aircraft was equal or superior to the highly touted Fokker, and in combat, allied aircraft found it to be a fierce competitor in the hands of competent pilots. Unfortunately, its late debut and the reputation of the D.VII effectively killed whatever opportunities the D.XII may have had to develop the reputation it purportedly deserved.

The basic armament package of the D.XII consisted of two fixed, synchronized Spandau machine guns mounted just ahead of the cockpit and firing forward through the propeller disk.

Champlin's Pfalz is an authentic World War I aircraft, veteran not only of the First World War but of many harrowing film epics thereafter. It is one of four such aircraft extant, the only one in a private collection. It was apparently damaged while under Allied testing, and the earliest pictures suggest the tail and upper center wing section may be grafts from another airframe.

Two such aircraft were brought to the U.S. for evaluation. Both were eventually civilian owned, and used side-by-side in film epics like *Dawn Patrol* (1931). Colonel J.B. Jarrett then bought this Pfalz and displayed it for many years in his Atlantic City amusement park.

Hollywood pilot Frank Tallman acquired the Pfalz in 1958, and Robert Rust of Atlanta restored it, replacing more than half the airframe's wooden structure, but returning the aircraft to flying status in less than a year.

Tallman auctioned off most of the collection in 1968. The aircraft was acquired by Wings and Wheels Museum in Orlando, Florida, until Champlin acquired title in 1981. The D.XII is no longer flown, though licensed and maintained in an airworthy condition.

collection. Eventually it went to Wings and Wheels Museum in Orlando, Florida, run by Korean War ace Dolph Overton. I purchased the Pfalz at auction in 1981 and it was fully restored by the museum staff. Like the *Wildcat*, it was a "movie star", appearing in World War I aviation films of the 1930s.

DOUG'S COMMENTS:

Our Pfalz D.XII was captured by U.S. forces in 1918 and became part of the Col. G.B. Jarrett

The Pfalz D.XII was equipped with dual-Spandau machine guns mounted just above and aft of the engine.

The Museum's Pfalz D.XII cockpit.

The Museum's Pfalz D.XII is an immaculately restored original airframe and apparently one of two Pfalz D.XIIs brought to the US following the cessation of WWI hostilities.

43

SPECIFICATIONS:

MANUFACTURER: Royal Aircraft Factory
DESIGNATION: S.E.5a
FORMAL NAME: none
SERVICE/TYPE/NO. CREW: Royal Flying Corps fighter/single-seat
COUNTRY OF ORIGIN: Great Britain
SERVED FROM/TO: 1917 through 1918
LENGTH: 20 ft. 11 in.
WINGSPAN/WING AREA: 26 ft. 7.4 in./ 245.8 sq. ft.
HEIGHT: 9 ft. 6 in.
EMPTY WEIGHT: 1,531 lbs.

GROSS WEIGHT: 2,048 lbs.
MAX. SPEED: 126 mph at 10,000 ft.
MAX. RANGE: 2½ hours endurance
MAX. ALTITUDE: 17,000 ft.
ENGINE MANUFACTURER: Hispano-Suiza
ENGINE DESIGNATION: 220 hp
ENGINE TYPE: Water-cooled V-8
POWER RATING: 220 hp
REGISTRATION/SERIAL NO.: NX910AV (reproduction)
NUMBER BUILT: approx. 5,200

Dressed in US markings, an S.E. 5A cruises at altitude. This pursuit was considered one WWI's very best.

ROYAL AIRCRAFT FACTORY S.E.5A

The prototype S.E.5 was designed by H.P. Folland and built around a new Hispano-Suiza engine that which had been imported from France during 1915. The first aircraft was completed during December of 1916 and flown for the first time later that same month.

Production was initiated almost immediately, and during March of 1917, the first production

A Royal Flying Corps S.E. 5A. in typical markings.

S.E. 5A with a single Lewis and a single Vickers.

S.E.5s were delivered to front-line units. Following a period of adjustment and modification, the aircraft was quick to prove itself suitable as an air combat mount. Consequent to this, Hispano-Suiza introduced a geared, 200 hp version of their earlier engine, and this was immediately adopted for use in production S.E.5s. The resulting changes led to what became known as the S.E.5a, and all following production aircraft were built to this standard.

Though engine difficulties haunted the S.E.5a for several months following its introduction these were eventually rectified and the type soon became a highly regarded mount for British pursuit pilots. Some of the greatest of all World War I aces utilized the S.E. 5a in combat, including Maj. Edward Mannock with 73 victories (50 in the S.E. 5a), Lt. Col. Billy Bishop, and Capt. James McCudden. They considered the aircraft's unbeatable strength and stability to be its greatest attributes, though it was similarly capable in speed and maneuverability.

Following World War I, the S.E.5 rapidly was phased out of service. A few were utilized in postwar assignments by the Australian and Canadian air forces and some fifty were manufactured in the U.S. as S.E.5Es by the Eberhardt company, but by the mid-1920s, the type was rarely seen.

The armament package fitted to most production aircraft consisted of a Vickers gun mounted in front of the cockpit on the port side and a Lewis gun mounted above the center section. The Vickers gun was synchronized to fire

through the propeller disk.

The Museum's S.E.5a is an elegant replica, built by the late Tom Davis and Bobby Strahlmann. Inside and out, it is produced precisely as the airplane was intended to be built in 1918. The aircraft arrived at Falcon Field in September 1988, and went on display in early 1989.

The aircraft is painted to depict the aircraft of ace George A. Vaughn, an American on duty with Number 84 Squadron, R.F.C., on August 22, 1918, the day he scored his fifth aerial victory to enter the ranks of the aces.

DOUG'S COMMENTS:

Latest additon to the World War I set is the superb S.E.5a, completed in 1989. It was one of three begun by Bobby Strahlmann, Tom Davis and Gil Bodine of Florida in 1971, and unfortunately was completed after Tom's untimely death. However, CFM had the distinct pleasure of honoring the builders as well as America's top surviving World War I ace, George Vaughn. At the 1989 dedication we were able to reunite Col. Vaughn with his mount 71 years after he achieved acedom in an S.E. bearing these markings. The evening was topped off with the presence of two other World War I aces, Ray Brooks and Douglas Campbell. Sadly, Col. Vaughn died three months later, but the privilege of hosting America's last three World War I aces will always remain.

The Museum's S.E. 5A cockpit.

The Museum's S.E.5A is a perfect replica of the original and is painted in the markings of the Royal Flying Corp's No. 84 Squadron.

SPECIFICATIONS:

MANUFACTURER: Rumpler (et.al.)
DESIGNATION: none
FORMAL NAME: *Taube*
SERVICE/TYPE/NO. CREW: German Air Force fighter/observation platform/bomber/single-seat
COUNTRY OF ORIGIN: Germany
SERVED FROM/TO: 1910 through 1914
LENGTH: 33 ft. 6 in.
WINGSPAN/WING AREA: 45 ft. 10 in./ 280 sq. ft. (approx.)
HEIGHT: 10 ft. 6 in.

EMPTY WEIGHT: 950 lbs.
GROSS WEIGHT: 1,200 lbs.
MAX. SPEED: 60 mph
MAX. RANGE: 4 hours endurance
MAX. ALTITUDE: 10,000 ft. approx.
ENGINE MANUFACTURER: Mercedes
ENGINE DESIGNATION: D.IIIa
ENGINE TYPE: six-cylinder water-cooled in-line
POWER RATING: 120 hp
REGISTRATION/SERIAL NO.: none (reproduction)
NUMBER BUILT: unknown

The "Taube" represents the oldest form of fighter technology in the Museum's extensive collection.

RUMPLER *TAUBE*

The *Taube* (German for "dove") monoplane series was the last of the pre-war first-generation aircraft to be utilized in combat, and as such, was quite antiquated from a technological standpoint by the time World War I broke out in Europe. Essentially of wood and fabric construction, it utilized wing-warping for roll control (rather than ailerons), and was built in such great variety and by so many different manufacturers, it remains very difficult, to this very day, to give a detailed overview of its history.

Among the better known manufacturers to produce the standard *Taube* design was the German Rumpler Flugzeug-Werke G.m.b.H., which had gained a modest reputation for building quality aircraft for sport and utilitarian duties. Included in the latter were select aircraft optimized for the military as observation platforms and these, in turn, generated small production contracts for the first of the Rumpler-built *Taubes*. These slow and somewhat cumbersome aircraft served the German Air Force during the early stages of World War I in the role of combat observation.

Virtually all *Taubes* were of essentially the same wing design and over-all planform. Construction was almost totally wood and fabric, with metal used sparingly in select places where only metal would suffice (wing fittings, engine mounting plates, landing gear parts, etc.). The cockpit was particularly spartan and provided only minimal instrumentation (which sometimes included only a rudimentary airspeed indicator and a recording barograph for altitude measurement!).

Within months of initial combat, the *Taube* was being phased out of front line service. By 1915, very few remained in service.

Armament, when it was provided, usually was in the form of hand-held weapons such as rifles or pistols.

The Museum's *Taube* was initiated by Art Williams in 1981 and completed in 1984.

DOUG'S COMMENTS:

Art Williams constructed the airframe in Germany and the Champlin Fighter Museum staff finished the cowling. The 120 hp Mercedes is extremely rare and was found in upstate New York.

The Museum's Rumpler "Taube" cockpit.

A Rumpler-manufactured "Taube" outside the company's plant in Germany during the early years of WWI.

The Museum's "Taube" is a near-exact replica. The original Mercedes engine, an extremely rare 120 hp version, was restored by Jim Appleby of California and Art Williams in Germany.

An original Royal Flying Corps Sopwith "Camel". Twin Vickers guns can be seen mounted above the cowling.

SPECIFICATIONS:

MANUFACTURER: Sopwith Aviation Company, Ltd.
DESIGNATION: F.1
FORMAL NAME: *Camel*
SERVICE/TYPE/NO. CREW: Royal Flying Corps fighter/single-seat
COUNTRY OF ORIGIN: Great Britain
SERVED FROM/TO: 1917 through 1918
LENGTH: 18 ft. 9 in.
WINGSPAN/WING AREA: 28 ft. 0 in./ 231 sq. ft.
HEIGHT: 8 ft. 6 in.

EMPTY WEIGHT: 962 lbs.
GROSS WEIGHT: 1,482 lbs.
MAX. SPEED: 104.5 mph at 10,000 ft.
MAX. RANGE: 2½ hour endurance
MAX. ALTITUDE: 18,000 ft.
ENGINE MANUFACTURER: Clerget
ENGINE DESIGNATION: 9B
ENGINE TYPE: nine-cylinder air-cooled rotary
POWER RATING: 130 hp
REGISTRATION/SERIAL NO.: NX6330 (replica)
NUMBER BUILT: 5,490

SOPWITH F.1 *CAMEL*

The first prototype of what was to become Sir Thomas Sopwith's most famous product was rolled out for the first time on December 22, 1916. This first *Camel*, developed from the smaller and significantly more docile Sopwith *Pup*, was a somewhat stumpy looking biplane of conventional construction and exceptional performance.

The *Camel* was ordered into production shortly after the unveiling of the first aircraft, and by the summer of 1917, the first production aircraft were being made available to operational squadrons. The first *Camels* to see action were those of the Royal Naval Air Service when, on July 4, 1917, five *Camels* attacked sixteen German *Gotha* bombers following a bombing run on Harwich, England.

As the type became more readily available to operational units, combat statistics soared and its reputation began to grow. Many competent pilots found the *Camel* to be an exceptional fighter, but others of lesser skill also found it to be intolerant of mistakes and downright dangerous if not flown with some measure of attention.

In the right hands, the *Camel* was an effective weapon. It was highly maneuverable, well armed, and quick enough to work one-on-one with any enemy aircraft. Only the Fokker Dr.I triplane was an even match in the maneuverability arena. The *Camel* eventually eliminated no less than 1,294 enemy aircraft—and thus set a record for the greatest number of aircraft destroyed by a single type during World War I.

A large number of experimental *Camels* were built and flown by Sopwith throughout the latter half of the war. Engines of varying types were tested in great number, and one *Camel* was built with tapered wings.

Champlin bought this aircraft from Antique Aero Limited of Riverside, California, in 1979. Jim and Zona Appleby changed the original pattern only slightly, adding brakes, instruments, and a tailwheel to this aircraft, which was intended for reliability and safety during commercial and promotional uses.

DOUG'S COMMENTS:

Of the World War I replicas, the Sopwith *Camel* came from the prolific Appleby stable while the two other Fokkers were acquired independently. Dr. Richard Couglin of New York worked from 1958 to 1972 to produce his full-scale Dr.I triplane, which I acquired in 1978.

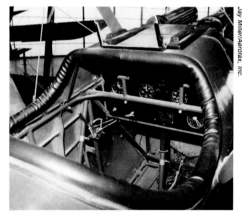

The Museum's Sopwith "Camel" cockpit.

A Sopwith "Camel" lifts off from the deck of the HMS "Pegasus" during mid-1918 carrier trials.

The Museum's Sopwith ''Camel'' is an authentic replica differing from the original aircraft primarily in having a radial instead of a rotary engine, tailwheel and brakes.

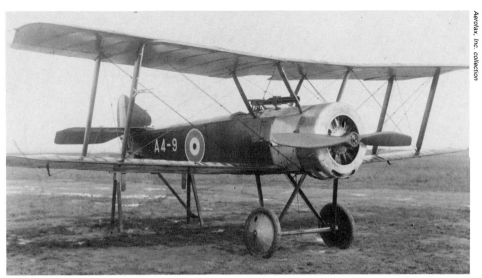
Aerofax, Inc. collection

The Sopwith "Pup" was one of the most popular pursuits of its day and was maneuverable and quick.

SOPWITH *PUP*

SPECIFICATIONS:

MANUFACTURER: Sopwith Aviation Company, Ltd.
DESIGNATION: none
FORMAL NAME: *Pup*
SERVICE/TYPE/NO. CREW: Royal Flying Corps fighter/single-seat
COUNTRY OF ORIGIN: Great Britain
SERVED FROM/TO: 1916 through 1917
LENGTH: 19 ft. 3¾ in.
WINGSPAN/WING AREA: 26 ft. 6 in./ 254 sq. ft.
HEIGHT: 9 ft. 5 in.

EMPTY WEIGHT: 787 lbs.
GROSS WEIGHT: 1,225 lbs.
MAX. SPEED: 111.5 mph
MAX. RANGE: 1¾ hours endurance
MAX. ALTITUDE: 18,500 ft.
ENGINE MANUFACTURER: Le Rhone
ENGINE DESIGNATION: 9C
ENGINE TYPE: nine-cylinder air-cooled rotary
POWER RATING: 80 hp
REGISTRATION/SERIAL NO.: NX6018 (reproduction)
NUMBER BUILT: approx. 1,770

Some have called the Sopwith *Pup* the most perfect flying machine ever made. No matter the accuracy of this statement, there is little doubt it was a docile and enjoyable aircraft to fly, and one greatly admired by its pilots. The name *Pup* (not chosen by Sopwith) was antithetical to everything the aircraft was designed to be. A true pursuit, it was capable of competing one-on-one with any air combat aircraft in the sky at the time

of its debut during the spring of 1916, and by September, not only was it in full production, it also was entering combat. A kill was in fact scored on September 24.

During its initial confrontations with the Germans, the *Pup* quickly proved itself superior to virtually every aircraft in German Air Force service. Its reputation spread so quickly, in fact, German pilots, until the advent of more capable

German aircraft types, purposefully avoided aerial combat with it unless given no other option.

Unfortunately, the rapid development of aircraft designs that was ongoing during 1916 and 1917 had caught up with the *Pup* by the autumn of 1917, and by the end of the year, it was being phased-out in favor of more capable aircraft.

The *Pup* participated in a variety of experiments involving operations from ship decks, and in so doing, became a testbed for future aircraft carrier criteria. Work on arresting gear, landing gear, and related items was undertaken with significant intensity utilizing modified *Pups*, and all eventually contributed to the later successes enjoyed by British carrier-borne aviation.

The *Pup's* armament package consisted of one fixed, synchronized Vickers machine gun mounted on top of the forward fuselage, ahead of the cockpit, and firing through the propeller disk. Miscellaneous other machine gun installations were tested and some *Pups* were equipped to carry small bombs on the landing gear axle. Still others were modified to fire rockets from the interplane struts.

The Museum's *Pup* is one of Carl Swanson's masterpieces, virtually indistinguishable from an original. Champlin purchased it in 1979 from James Ricklef of San Carlos, California.

DOUG'S COMMENTS:

Certainly one of the finest reproduction craftsmen in the world is Carl Swanson of Darien, Wisconsin. He provided two of our four Sop-

withs: the *Pup* via Jim Ricklef of California, and the *Triplane*, plus the Nieuport 27 as well. All feature original rotary engines, appropriate instruments and armament. The only concession to modern operations on any of these faithful products is a wheel built into the Nieuport's tail skid.

Jay Miller/Aerofax, Inc.

The Museum's Sopwith "Pup" cockpit.

Aerofax, Inc. collection

The Sopwith "Pup" was on occasion flown from carriers during the latter stages of WWI.

The Museum's Sopwith ''Pup'' is a reproduction of the original aircraft, with the LeRhone rotary engine.

The Sopwith "Snipe" is considered by many authorities to be the finest Allied pursuit of WWI.

SPECIFICATIONS:

MANUFACTURER: Sopwith Aviation Company, Ltd.
DESIGNATION: 7F.1
FORMAL NAME: *Snipe*
SERVICE/TYPE/NO. CREW: Royal Flying Corps. fighter/single-seat
COUNTRY OF ORIGIN: Great Britain
SERVED FROM/TO: 1918 through 1919
LENGTH: 19 ft. 10 in.
WINGSPAN/WING AREA: 31 ft. 1 in./ 271 sq. ft.
HEIGHT: 8 ft. 3 in.

EMPTY WEIGHT: 1.312 lbs.
GROSS WEIGHT: 2,020 lbs.
MAX. SPEED: 121 mph at 10,000 ft.
MAX. RANGE: 3 hour endurance
MAX. ALTITUDE: 19,500 ft.
ENGINE MANUFACTURER: Bentley
ENGINE DESIGNATION: B.R.2
ENGINE TYPE: nine-cylinder air-cooled rotary
POWER RATING: 230 hp
REGISTRATION/SERIAL NO.: NX6765D (replica)
NUMBER BUILT: approx. 500

SOPWITH 7F.1 *SNIPE*

The success of the Sopwith *Camel* and the development of a new and powerful rotary engine, the B.R.2, led to the birth of a new Sopwith pursuit designated the 7F.1 and named *Snipe*. It was intended that this aircraft should serve as a replacement for its renowned predecessor, and as a result, Sopwith aspired to create an aircraft with exceptional performance.

The first *Snipe* was tested during late 1917 utilizing the smaller B.R.1 engine. Several additional prototypes were manufactured and tested during the following several months, and by the early spring of 1918, orders for over 1,800 *Snipes* from six different manufacturers had been signed.

The first production aircraft were delivered during the summer of 1918, and as the type began to accumulate operational experience, it became apparent that it was quite similar to the *Camel* in most performance areas, but was superior in rate of climb and handling.

Very few *Snipes* actually saw combat due to the type's late arrival in the war, but at least one famous episode of air combat was accomplished with the type: Maj. W.G. Barker won a Victoria Cross for his October 27, 1918 mission which resulted in the destruction of at least four enemy aircraft (he was shot three times in the process, and crash landed following the last engagement of the mission). Though it was utilized only to a limited extent at the end of the war, numerous authorities have concluded that the *Snipe* almost certainly was the best Allied pursuit aircraft of the period.

The *Snipe's* armament package consisted of two Vickers guns mounted above and behind the engine and synchronized to fire forward through the propeller disk.

The Museum's *Snipe* was constructed by replica and antique builder Richard Day of Colonia, New Jersey. Finished in 1982, it is an authentic, full-scale replica of a postwar *Snipe* in RAF service. However, for reasons of safety, the engine is a 220 hp Continental radial of nearly identical size and power output.

DOUG'S COMMENTS:

Our third Sopwith is a *Snipe* built by Dick Day, an FAA employee in New Jersey. The *Snipe*, powered by a Continental radial engine but otherwise fully authentic, was flown for one season at Cole Palen's Old Rhinebeck, N.Y. airdrome.

The Museum's Sopwith "Snipe" cockpit.

The Museum's Sopwith "Snipe" is an authentic replica with the exception of its radial rather than rotary engine. It is painted in typical post-World War I Royal Air Force markings.

Sopwith's superb "Triplane" was the first of many three-winged WWI pursuits, and possibly the most successful.

SPECIFICATIONS:

MANUFACTURER: Sopwith Aviation Company, Ltd.
DESIGNATION: none
FORMAL NAME: *Triplane*
SERVICE/TYPE/NO. CREW: Royal Flying Corps fighter/single-seat
COUNTRY OF ORIGIN: Great Britain
SERVED FROM/TO: 1916 through 1917
LENGTH: 26 ft. 6 in.
WINGSPAN/WING AREA: 19 ft. 4 in./ 231 sq. ft.
HEIGHT: 10 ft. 6 in.

EMPTY WEIGHT: 1,101 lbs.
GROSS WEIGHT: 1,541 lbs.
MAX. SPEED: 117 mph at 5,000 ft.
MAX. RANGE: 2 hours endurance
MAX. ALTITUDE: 20,500 ft.
ENGINE MANUFACTURER: Clerget
ENGINE DESIGNATION: 9B
ENGINE TYPE: nine-cylinder air-cooled rotary
POWER RATING: 130 hp
REGISTRATION/SERIAL NO.: N38057 (reproduction)
NUMBER BUILT: approx. 175

SOPWITH *TRIPLANE*

The precedent setting Sopwith *Triplane*, when it first appeared during late 1916, was the most maneuverable production fighter in the world. Its affect on German designs was profound, and within months, virtually every German manufacturer of note, including Albatros, Brandenburg, Fokker, Lohner, Pfalz, and Roland, had developed or was flight testing a triplane fighter.

Sopwith's original objective in developing their revolutionary aircraft was to give the pilot not only a highly maneuverable platform, but also one which gave the pilot a better over-all field of view. The latter was accomplished by strategic placement of the wings, and by keeping the wing chords small. Maneuverability objectives also were achieved, as it later was determined in actual combat that the *Triplane* was unbelievably nimble and quick; pilots were unanimously praiseworthy of its dog-fighting attributes.

Following flight testing during mid-1916, the *Triplane* was ordered into production by the Royal Naval Air Service and the Royal Flying Corps. Because of the exigencies of war, all *Triplanes* eventually went to the R.N.A.S. only. Deliveries actually were initiated to the service during late 1916, and by April of the following year, operational sorties were being flown.

Actual combat took place for the first time on April 22, when two *Triplanes* met a formation of fifteen German aircraft. In the ensuing battle, three of the German machines were destroyed. The two *Triplanes* returned to their home field unscathed.

Though the *Triplane's* successes were numerous and seemingly unending, by August of 1917 it was being rapidly phased out of R.N.A.S. service and replaced by Sopwith *Camels*. Many pilots were unhappy with this development, but there was little they could do to change it. By the end of the year, the *Triplane* had all but disappeared from the skies over Europe.

Normal *Triplane* armament consisted of a single fixed Vickers machine gun mounted in the center of the upper fuselage ahead of the cockpit and synchronized to fire through the propeller disk. Some aircraft were equipped with two Vickers machine guns.

The Museum's *Tripe* is an extremely accurate and authentic depiction of Sub-Lieutenant Mel Alexander's "Black Prince". This young Canadian claimed acedom in *Triplanes*, and added another thirteen kills in *Camels*. The aircraft's engine was carefully built up from two 130 hp Clergets. The plane was built in twenty-two short months by Carl Swanson of Darien, Wisconsin, who also built the Museum's *Pup*. The same elaborate attention to detail is manifest in the *Triplane*.

The Museum's Sopwith "Triplane" cockpit.

The Sopwith "Triplane" proved exceptionally maneuverable, but its lack of speed eventually led to its demise.

The Museum's Sopwith "Triplane" is a reproduction with an original Clerget rotary engine and original gun and instruments.

The S.P.A.D. XIII was one of the most technologically and mechanically complex pursuits of WWI.

Aerofax, Inc. collection

SPECIFICATIONS:

MANUFACTURER: S.P.A.D. (Societe' Anonyme Pour L'Aviation et ses De'rive's)
DESIGNATION: XIII
FORMAL NAME: none
SERVICE/TYPE/NO. CREW: Aviation Militaire fighter/single-seat
COUNTRY OF ORIGIN: France
SERVED FROM/TO: 1917 through 1918
LENGTH: 20 ft. 4 in.
WINGSPAN/WING AREA: 26 ft. 3¾ in./ 227 sq. ft.
HEIGHT: 7 ft. 6½ in.
EMPTY WEIGHT: 1,245 lbs.

GROSS WEIGHT: 1,807 lbs.
MAX. SPEED: 138 mph
MAX. RANGE: 2 hour endurance
MAX. ALTITUDE: 21,820 ft.
ENGINE MANUFACTURER: Hispano-Suiza
ENGINE DESIGNATION: 8BE
ENGINE TYPE: eight-cylinder, water-cooled V-8
POWER RATING: 220 hp
REGISTRATION/SERIAL NO.: NX3883F (reproduction)
NUMBER BUILT: approx. 8,470

S.P.A.D. XIII

The S.P.A.D. XIII was perhaps the most famous French fighter to be utilized in combat during World War I. Designed during the last few months of 1916 by M. Becherau, it was an evolutionary development of his earlier, successful S.P.A.D. S.VII, but differed in having unequal-chord ailerons, rounded tail surface tips, and other refinements. Additionally, inverted vee-shaped front center section struts were added between the wing and fuselage. Like its smaller predecessor, the S.P.A.D. XIII was powered by the dependable Hispano-Suiza V-8 producing from 200 to 235 hp.

The S.P.A.D. XIII began replacing the S.VII in frontline service during the summer and fall of 1917. By the beginning of the following year, it had become the standard French single-seat pursuit. It also was becoming quite popular with U.S. pilots of the American Expeditionary Forces as it was rugged, fast, and well armed. The most famous U.S. pilot, Capt. Edward Rickenbacker, was quick to put the S.P.A.D. XIII to work on his way to a total of 26 aerial victories.

French, Italian, and Belgian units eventually flew the S.P.A.D. XIII in combat. It remained in French service until 1923 before being replaced by newer and more advanced fighters.

The S.P.A.D. XIII's armament package usually consisted of two synchronized Vickers machine guns mounted just ahead of the cockpit and firing forward through the propeller disk.

This specimen was built by Richard Day of Colonia, New Jersey. Final assembly and completion of the aircraft was executed in the Champlin Museum. It is an authentic, full-scale replica of Luke's aircraft, including a genuine Hisso engine. The 27th Pursuit Squadron markings are typical of S.P.A.D.s from that unit.

DOUG'S COMMENTS:

Dick Day is also responsible for most of our splendid S.P.A.D. XIII. It was a lengthy, difficult project since the design is among the most complex of all World War I fighters. The original drawings were destroyed in World War II, so Dick resorted to measurement of S.P.A.D.s owned by Palen and the National Air and Space Museum. Upon delivery of the airframe, Herb Tischler of Fort Worth completed the metalwork, particularly the complicated cowling. Our museum staff rendered the finishing touches—the markings of Lt. Frank Luke, the "Arizona Balloon Buster".

Jay Miller/Aerofax, Inc.

The Museum's S.P.A.D. XIII cockpit.

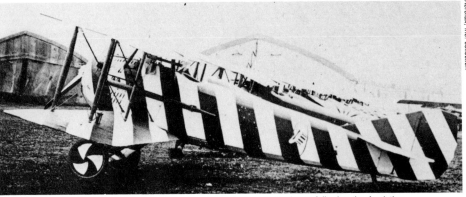

Aerofax, Inc. collection

Eddie Rickenbacker's S.P.A.D. XIII was given an unusual striped paint scheme following the Armistice.

The Museum's S.P.A.D. XIII reproduction with the original Hispano-Suiza engine, guns and instruments.

Jack Fellow's superb painting depicting the surrendering of the Museum's Focke-Wulf Fw 190D-13 to the British at the end of World War II.

WORLD WAR II

The photos and information in this section of the book pertain to the aircraft currently on display in the Champlin Fighter Museum. We have attempted also to integrate material relating to the gun systems carried by these aircraft wherever such items relate to our gun collection.

Aerofax, Inc. collection

SPECIFICATIONS:

MANUFACTURER: Curtiss-Wright Corp.	**EMPTY WEIGHT:** 6,000 lbs.
DESIGNATION: P-40N	**GROSS WEIGHT:** 8,850 lbs.
FORMAL NAME: *Warhawk*	**MAX. SPEED:** 378 mph at 10,500 ft.
SERVICE/TYPE/NO. CREW: Army Air Corps fighter/single-seat	**MAX. RANGE:** 750 miles
COUNTRY OF ORIGIN: U.S.A.	**MAX. ALTITUDE:** 38,000 ft.
SERVED FROM/TO: 1940 through 1945	**ENGINE MANUFACTURER:** Allison
LENGTH: 33 ft. 4 in.	**ENGINE DESIGNATION:** V-1710-81
WINGSPAN/WING AREA: 37 ft. 4 in./ 236 sq. ft.	**ENGINE TYPE:** twelve-cylinder liquid-cooled V
HEIGHT: 12 ft. 4 in.	**POWER RATING:** 1,360 hp
	REGISTRATION/SERIAL NO.: NL10626/44-4192
	NUMBER BUILT: approx. 13,700

The Curtiss P-40 "Warhawk" was one of the most famous yet least successful fighters to participate in WWII.

CURTISS P-40N *WARHAWK*

Unquestionably one of the best-known U.S. combat aircraft of World War II, the P-40 series eventually had the distinction of becoming the last of a long line of Curtiss *Hawk* named aircraft. By the end of the war, the P-40 had operated on virtually every front and consequently had served with the air forces of the majority of U.S. allies. Perhaps even more importantly, the P-40 become the third most-produced U.S. fighter of the war, being numerically inferior only to the *Mustang* and *Thunderbolt*.

The P-40 began life as a V-type liquid-cooled engine derivative of the air-cooled radial-engined Curtiss P-36. An Allison V-1710 replaced the P-36's R-1830, and the resulting aircraft, known at Curtiss as the *Hawk* 81, made its first flight during October of 1938. Following tests conducted at Wright Field during 1939, an order for 524 P-40s (subsequently reduced to 200) was placed by the Air Corps.

A large number of P-40s eventually went to the British (via Lend-Lease agreements) under the *Tomahawk* designation. In the interim, P-40Bs and P-40Cs, offering upgraded armor and armament, were released for Air Corps service. The type entered overseas service with the U.S. military for the first time during July of 1941, and a number of *Warhawks* both participated in and were destroyed during the December 7, 1941, Japanese attack on Pearl Harbor.

The P-40's most memorable World War II combat experience was its use by the pilots of Gen Claire Chennault's American Volunteer Group (AVG), oftentimes referred to simply as the "Flying Tigers". This mercenary unit served in the defense of China against Japanese aggressors during a period from 1941 through 1942 while operating three squadrons from Kunming. On July 4, 1942, the AVG was absorbed into the Air Force and formally named the 23rd Pursuit Group. As the AVG it was credited with the destruction of 286 Japanese aircraft (for a loss of 23 American pilots).

The P-40D now followed the earlier models into production, this being the first major redesign of the type since its introduction. Equipped with an Allison V-1710-39, its propeller gear box arrangement permitted a shorter and somewhat stubbier fuselage design. Other changes included a revised armament complement, repositioning of the radiator, and shortened landing gear struts. Most P-40Ds went to the British.

The P-40E with improved armament, increased gross weight, and slightly lower top speed, was next, and the majority of these went on to serve with the Air Force in Europe and

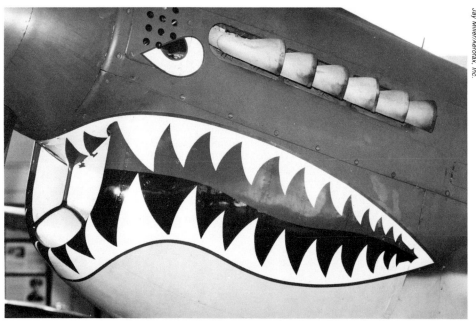
Jay Miller/Aerofax, Inc.

The Museum's P-40N bears shark-mouth markings made famous by Gen. Claire Chennault's "Flying Tigers".

Jay Miller/Aerofax, Inc.

The Museum's Curtiss P-40N cockpit.

North Africa. The P-40F, with a Packard-built version of the British Rolls Royce V-1650 *Merlin*, followed in two versions, one with a short and one with a 20 inch longer fuselage. The P-40K, though heavier, was similar to the P-40F, though powered by an Allison V-1710-73 engine. At 10,000 lbs., it was the heaviest of all production P-40 versions. The P-40L was a stripped P-40F, offering a weight savings of 250 lbs. at gross weight and the loss of two wing guns.

The modest performance improvements resulting from the P-40F weight reduction program encouraged Curtiss to pursue further weight savings and the resulting aircraft was the P-40N. Equipped with four wing-mounted machine guns, no front fuselage fuel tank, and other miscellaneous weight saving measures, it became the most-produced (5,220) of all *Warhawks* variants and also the fastest, at 378 mph.

Scattered between the various major *Warhawk* production models was a large assortment of prototypes, testbeds, and limited production two-seat trainers. By 1945, the P-40 was considered a seriously outmoded fighter, and was removed quickly from the active Air Force inventory following cessation of hostilities.

Armament packages for the P-40 typically consisted of two or six .50 cal. machine guns mounted in wing and nose compartments. In the P-40B, a pair of .30 cal. machine guns was paired with two .50 cal. machine guns. Additionally, all *Warhawks*, from the P-40F on, could carry external ordnance on wing pylons.

The Museum's aircraft probably has fewer than sixty total hours. It was flown direct from the manufacturer to storage in Tucson. It sat for many years on display at Griffith Park in Los Angeles, until Frank Tallman acquired it and loaned the plane to the San Diego Aerospace Museum for their Flying Tiger display. Tallman sold the P-40 to Champlin in 1972. Dick Martin of Carlsbad, California delivered the overhauled aircraft in 1979, painted in correct Nationalist Chinese markings.

DOUG'S COMMENTS:

Certainly the lowest-time P-40 in the world, and perhaps the lowest-time warbird, is our N model. In 1944 it was flown straight from the Curtiss-Wright factory in Buffalo, N.Y. to storage in Arizona. By that time the P-40 was an obsolete aircraft, and consequently its military flight time was limited to acceptance tests and the cross-country.

Following the war the fighter was donated to Los Angeles County and became a pigeon roost in Griffith Park. Eventually the late Frank Tallman acquired the *Warhawk* and loaned it to the San Diego Aerospace Museum. I purchased it in 1974. A four-year restoration was undertaken by

Jay Miller/Aerofax, Inc.

The "Warhawk's" most famous contribution to the war effort was through its use by Gen. Claire Chennault's American Volunteer Group—also known as the "Flying Tigers".

Dick Martin at Carlsbad, California, and we flew the P-40 to Mesa in 1980. That was its last flight, making a grand total of some 50 hours.

Champlin collection

The Museum's Focke Wulf Fw 190D-13 as it appeared at the end of WWII and prior to its shipment to the U.S.

SPECIFICATIONS:

MANUFACTURER: Focke-Wulf Flugzeugbau
DESIGNATION: Fw 190D-12
FORMAL NAME: none
SERVICE/TYPE/NO. CREW: Luftwaffe
ground-attack fighter/single-seat
COUNTRY OF ORIGIN: Germany
SERVED FROM/TO: 1940 through 1945
LENGTH: 33 ft. 5¼ in.
WINGSPAN/WING AREA: 34 ft. 5⅓ in.
HEIGHT: 11 ft. ¼ in.
EMPTY WEIGHT: 7,750 lbs.

GROSS WEIGHT: 11,000 lbs.
MAX. SPEED: 426 mph at 21,650 ft.
MAX. RANGE: 520 miles
MAX. ALTITUDE: 38,810 ft.
ENGINE MANUFACTURER: Junkers-Jumo
ENGINE DESIGNATION: 213F
ENGINE TYPE: twelve-cylinder
liquid cooled V
POWER RATING: 2,060 hp
REGISTRATION/SERIAL NO. NX190D/836017
NUMBER BUILT: approx. 20,000

FOCKE-WULF Fw 190D-13

The Focke-Wulf Fw 190D-13 represents the penultimate development of what many consider to be the finest German piston-engined fighter of World War II. When the original production Fw 190s appeared over the skies of Europe for the first time during the autumn of 1941, there is little question they represented the most advanced air combat aircraft in the world. Fast, powerful, agile, and heavily armed, the Focke-Wulf fighters, designed by the inimitable Kurt Tank, were the nemesis of every Allied aircraft in the skies. Many months would pass before an Allied aircraft with comparable performance and handling would be available to fight them.

Birth of the Fw 190 can be traced back to a Luftwaffe requirment calling for a single-seat interceptor that could be used to supplement the seemingly unbeatable Messerschmitt Bf 109. Kurt Tank was assigned to head the design team, and the resulting aircraft, powered by a 1,550 hp BMW 139 eighteen-cylinder radial engine, proved quite radical for its day.

The prototype Fw 190, piloted by Hans Sander, took to the air for the first time on June 1, 1939. Sander's initial impressions, other than experiencing difficulties with engine overheating, were extremely favorable, and as a result, the Luftwaffe began generating plants to get the aircraft into production.

A series of prototype and testbed aircraft followed, with the first of 30 pre-production aircraft being ordered during late 1940. By March of 1941, an initial production batch was being delivered to a Luftwaffe test unit, and on September 27, the type entered combat against a small contingent of British *Spitfires* Vs for the first time. This engagement quickly verified the superiority of the Fw 190, as it proved more maneuverable and significantly faster. The *Spitfire* was capable only of turning a tighter circle than the new Focke-Wulf.

Many production versions and thousands of airframes followed these initial Fw 190As into the skies over Europe and North Africa, and whenever they met Allied aircraft, they proved extraordinarily competitive in the hands of competent pilots. By mid-1944, versions of the Fw 190 powered by radial engines of 2,000 and more horsepower were commonplace, and performance remained on-par with anything then being produced by the Allies. The aircraft not only proved competent as an air combat platform, but also as a ground support weapon as well, and during North African service often was utilized to attack Allied troops, ground emplacements, and military equipment.

Mid-way through the war, Kurt Tank and his Focke-Wulf design team began exploring propulsion options other than the original radial engine scheme that remained in use in production aircraft. One of the original prototype studies had, in fact, called for a V-type liquid-cooled engine, and this configuration was resurrected starting with the Fw 190V-13 testbed. Powered by a Daimler-Benz DB 603A 12-cylinder engine and equipped with an unusual nose-mounted annular radiator (thus giving the aircraft the look of the radial-engined version), this aircraft became the first Fw 190 variant to fly with a liquid-cooled engine, and thus the progenitor of a lengthy production series that would result in the most advanced, and fastest of all Fw 190s, the Tank Ta 152 series.

Jay Miller/Aerofax, Inc.

The Fw 190D-13 final restoration process was completed by Museum personnel during early 1990.

Jay Miller/Aerofax, Inc.

The Museum's Focke Wulf Fw 190D-13 cockpit.

Following the Fw 190V-13, a number of additional liquid-cooled prototypes and testbeds were completed, these being followed by the first production model designated Fw 190D-9. Though somewhat more vulnerable to attack than its radial-engined stable-mates, this aircraft offered considerably better performance at high altitude, and by the end of the war, was considered by many Luftwaffe pilots to have been Germany's finest operational fighter.

A series of prototypes were interjected into the series of Fw 190D sub-types that rolled from Focke-Wulf production lines, but during late 1944, a prototype referred to as the Fw 190V65 and powered by a 2,060 hp Jumo 213F liquid-cooled V-12 was completed and test flown. This aircraft quickly led to orders for a production version referred to as the Fw 190D-12, which originally had been optimized to serve as a ground attack aircraft. Equipped with two MG 151/20mm cannon in its wing roots and a single MK 108 firing through the propeller spinner, it also was provided with special armor plate around the engine compartment.

Production of the Fw 190D-12 and -13 series was initiated at the Arado and Fieseler aircraft manufacturing facilities during March of 1945, but only a select few aircraft were completed prior to the cessation of hostilities. The Fw 190D-12 had a 30mm MK108 cannon. The Fw 190D-13 had a hub gun mount for a 20mm MG151 (this difference was the telltale sign dictating the designation of the Champlin Museum's aircraft). Though one of the most advanced "production" fighters of the war and also one of the fastest (the Fw 190D-12/R21, equipped with an MW-50 water-methanol injection system is stated to have attained 453 mph at 36,000 ft.).

The extraordinary success of Kurt Tank's fighters, which included the Fw 190 family, eventually allowed him the unique honor of having an entire aircraft series given the Tank name. The most significant of these was the Tank Ta 152, a highly-advanced derivative of the Fw 190. In retrospect, it is apparent the Ta 152 was the ultimate Fw 190. Both long and short wing Ta 152s were built and flown, with the most advanced being the exotic-looking Ta 152H. This model, equipped with the Jumo 213E/B (Boosted) engine capable of generating 2,250 hp for short periods, was provided a pressurized cockpit and a very high-aspect-ratio wing of 47 ft. 7 inch span. Capable of 472 mph at 41,000 ft. it could achieve altitudes of 48,560 ft.— phenomenal performance figures for 1945.

Armament packages found in the various Fw 190 models were greatly varied and numerous. Normal gun complements often consisted of two MG 151/20 cannon and two MG 17 machine guns, but some aircraft were armed with up to six MG 151/20 or had two 30mm MK 103 cannon mounted under the wings. Additionally, a variety of bomb options was available, and some air-

After many years of restoration, the Champlin Museum's extremely rare Fw 190D-13 was completed and placed on display during early 1990.

craft carried rocket tubes and related weapons. Still other Fw 190s were seen with LT F5b torpedoes or LT 950 torpedoes mounted on centerline attachments.

By the end of production, just over 20,000 Fw 190s of all versions had been manufactured.

The Champlin Museum's Fw was delivered to JG-26 (*JagdGeschwader* approximates an allied fighter group) *Schlageter* (boxer, a nickname signified by the stylized Gothic "S" on the unit shield) in March 1945. By that stage of the war, few records were kept of what personnel were assigned to which aircraft, so little is known of its service record, save that the aircraft was actually assigned and test flown, as was customary before unit markings were affixed. The aircraft, as ordered by the Allied Truce Commission, was flown to Flensburg, near the Danish border, in May 1945. It is displayed in a reconstruction of its wartime markings, recorded as it stood at Flensburg.

Numbered FE-T-2-118 for inventory purposes, the aircraft was among five long noses brought to the United States for flight evaluation after the war. At some time after its delivery stateside, its wings were exchanged with another aircraft. It was likely not flown much, for not long after

Colonel Harold Watson brought the technical study units to this country, interest in Axis piston-engined aircraft research waned. The Fw was donated to Georgia Tech for aviation engineering research, and by 1955 had suffered much abuse and vandalism. After several changes of ownership in the 1950s and '60s, the aircraft showed up, partially assembled but with many parts missing, in Santa Barbara, California. Champlin purchased the aircraft in 1972.

Champlin shipped the aircraft back to Germany where, under the tutelage of Kurt Tank, A.A. Williams of Guenzburg executed a four-year restoration and preservation program. He fabricated anew many of the missing parts and gathered bits and pieces from all over Europe. Restoring this simple fighter required thousands of manhours.

Some of Williams' comments on the restoration are interesting, especially in view of the fact that the aircraft spent some fifteen years outdoors:

"The Fw is coming along nicely. But so many jury-rigged sheet metal problems! undoubtedly put together by slave labor[4]. There are rivets where just the head fills the hole, blind holes

drilled to maintain the pattern and fool the inspector. I found three of the original inspection covers stashed inside the wing, lost many years ago, perhaps during assembly, but like new. The old VDM aluminum is highly resistant to corrosion, unlike our 2024 series, and is a delight to work with. We have pulled the gear, and with a little cleaning, plus some new "O" rings, will proff o.k."

Art Williams
January 24, 1973

Thus, from a clan of more than 13,360 aircraft, via a most circuitous route, one original was restored and finished in 1976. As of this writing, the museum has two complete Jumo 213 E/F engines and a third usable as a core. Preparations are being made to start and run the engine now in the airframe. Two of the "power eggs" are complete with their radiators.

---

[4] By early 1945, conditions in the German aircraft industry were rather brutal, locally controlled by generally unsympathetic S.S. types whose sinister presence tended to turn the rush of production into a panic. Even skilled, experienced workers were sometimes severely punished for perceived inefficiencies. Thus, even in plants where there was little slave labor employed, quality control suffered.

Aerofax, Inc. collection

SPECIFICATIONS:

MANUFACTURER: General Motors (Eastern Aircraft Division)
DESIGNATION: FM-2
FORMAL NAME: *Wildcat*
SERVICE/TYPE/NO. CREW: Navy carrier-borne fighter/single-seat
COUNTRY OF ORIGIN: U.S.A.
SERVED FROM/TO: 1937 through 1945
LENGTH: 28 ft. 11 in.
WINGSPAN/WING AREA: 38 ft. 0 in./ 260 sq. ft.
HEIGHT: 11 ft. 5 in.

EMPTY WEIGHT: 5,448 lbs.
GROSS WEIGHT: 8,271 lbs.
MAX. SPEED: 332 mph at 28,800 ft.
MAX. RANGE: 900 miles
MAX. ALTITUDE: 34,700 ft.
ENGINE MANUFACTURER: Wright
ENGINE DESIGNATION: R-1820-56
ENGINE TYPE: nine-cylinder air-cooled radial
POWER RATING: 1,350 hp
REGISTRATION/SERIAL NO.: NL90523
NUMBER BUILT: approx. 8,000

Grumman's "Wildcat" was the first of a long line of successful "cat"-named monoplane pursuits.

GENERAL MOTORS FM-2 *WILDCAT*

Grumman's F4F *Wildcat*, which eventually was to be produced not only by Grumman, but also by General Motors (Eastern Aircraft Division), came to life as an advanced fighter biplane design study under the designation XF4F-1 during 1935. As part of a U.S. Navy fighter competition, it was forced to compete with a new Brewster monoplane designated F2A-1. Before metal was cut by Grumman on the first prototype, however, it had become apparent that the Brewster aircraft was the superior design. Accordingly, Grumman shifted gears and quickly moved ahead with a monoplane version of its original biplane study. On July 18, 1936, as the XF4F-2, it was ordered in prototype form by the Navy.

The first XF4F-2 took to the air for the first time on September 2, 1937, and over the next nine months, it was test flown against a variety of

Jay Miller/Aerofax, Inc.

Twin .50 cals. were mounted in each "Wildcat" wing.

aircraft including the F2A-1. The latter eventually won a production contract during 1938, but Grumman's design nevertheless proved too good to simply eliminate. Grumman now was given a contract to build an upgraded version of the F4F-2, and this aircraft, as the XF4F-3 with its significantly more powerful engine (Pratt & Whitney XR-1830-76), proved a winner.

During August of 1939, an initial Navy order for a production version of the F4F-3 was placed, and the first example was completed by the spring of the following year. Additional orders for the French (as the G-36A) and British military services (as the *Martlet*) now followed as a result of German aggression, and these aircraft were delivered ahead of what now were becoming an ever-expanding litany of U.S. Navy orders.

By the time of formal U.S. involvement in World War II, *Wildcats* had been delivered to a number of U.S. Navy and U.S. Marine Corps squadrons. These aircraft eventually entered combat for the first time against the Japanese during the post-December 7, 1941 period, having modest successes against a numerically and technologically superior air force. British *Martlets* also had been involved in combat against the Germans by this time, and likewise had had modest success against superior forces.

The first *Wildcat* with folding wings was the F4F-4, this version entering limited production during 1941, and full-scale production the following year. Consequent to this was the rare (only 20 built) F4F-7 variant optimized for reconnaissance and provided enough fuel for a range of well over 3,500 miles!

By early 1943, the *Wildcat* was perhaps the

most numerous U.S. Navy fighter, and undoubtedly its most important until the arrival of the superior Grumman F6F *Hellcat* and Vought F4U *Corsair*. It was a viable mount against a wide variety of enemy aircraft, and though perhaps not as agile or fast, it nevertheless proved extraordinarily rugged and dependable. Operating from a variety of large and small aircraft carriers, it could be found in Pacific, Atlantic, and Mediterranean waters, and was utilized with considerable success in a variety of roles for which it originally was not intended. Though technologically inferior to and lacking the performance of the superb Mitsubishi *Zero*, the *Wildcat* managed to hold its own during combat with this aircraft due in part to a superior armament complement and better piloting technique. By the end of the war, in combat with a wide variety of enemy aircraft types, the *Wildcat's* kill/loss ratio was 6.9 to 1.

The exigencies of war forced the U.S. defense industry to utilize a number of production resources that were not originally designed to accommodate aircraft. General Motors, one of the world's largest producers of automobiles, for instance, converted five of its Eastern Division manufacturing facilities to the Eastern Aircraft Division and there produced a version of the *Wildcat* under the designation FM-1. The first of these was delivered on August 31, 1942, and in less than a year, another 1000 or so had been completed.

Eastern later introduced the FM-2, which, with its more powerful engine (a Wright R-1820-56) and lower gross takeoff weight, permitted better take-off performance. This *Wildcat* version,

which was equipped with a distinctive, tall vertical fin and rudder (to improve directional control in consideration of the larger and more powerful engine), was optimized for use aboard the CVE escort carrier series and in fact was their primary complement throughout the rest of the war. In total, Eastern manufactured well in excess of 4,000 FM-2s and *Wildcat VIs* (British

Jay Miller/Aerofax, Inc.

The Museum's General Motors FM-2 cockpit.

version) by the time production ceased during 1944.

The standard *Wildcat* armament package consisted of either four or six .50 cal. wing-mounted machine guns. General Motors-manufactured aircraft also had the capability of carrying bombs or rockets on underwing attachment points.

The Museum's FM-2 is one of several aircraft here with minimal airframe total time. It saw service during World War II, primarily in fictional films, and never left the States. After very brief squadron duty, it passed through several civilian owners, until Champlin acquired it from William Whitesell in 1971. Total airframe time is about 600 hours.

DOUG'S COMMENTS:

Two Navy fighters came from Bill Whitesell of the Flying W Ranch in New Jersey. In 1971 I saw a *Wall Street Journal* ad, offering an FG-1D *Corsair* and FM-2 *Wildcat*, both in flying condition, and purchased them both. Though I sold the FG because I already had the F2G, I retained the *Wildcat*. It had never been an operational aircraft, being loaned to Paul Mantz for film making. After the war it sat in an Ottumwa, Iowa park where it was purchased in the early 60s by an East Coast corporate pilot. Eventually he parted with the FM but kept all the accessories. In 1987 he contacted me and offered the drop tanks, rocket rails and other hard-to-find items which now round out the scrappy little fighter.

Built by both Grumman and the Eastern Aircraft Division of General Motors, the F4F/FM "Wildcat" was the first modern carrier-capable fighter to be acquired by the US Navy.

Aerofax, Inc. collection

SPECIFICATIONS:

MANUFACTURER: Goodyear (Chance Vought)
DESIGNATION: F2G-1
FORMAL NAME: *Corsair*
SERVICE/TYPE/NO. CREW: Marine Corps ground support fighter/single-seat
COUNTRY OF ORIGIN: U.S.A.
SERVED FROM/TO: 1944 through early 1945
LENGTH: 33 ft. 9 in.
WINGSPAN/WING AREA: 41 ft. 0 in./ 314 sq. ft.
HEIGHT: 16 ft. 1 in.

EMPTY WEIGHT: 10,249 lbs.
GROSS WEIGHT: 15,422 lbs.
MAX. SPEED: 431 mph at 16,400 ft.
MAX. RANGE: 1,955 miles
MAX. ALTITUDE: 38,800 ft.
ENGINE MANUFACTURER: Pratt & Whitney
ENGINE DESIGNATION: R-4360-4
ENGINE TYPE: twenty-eight cylinder air-cooled radial
POWER RATING: 3,000 hp
REGISTRATION/SERIAL NO.: NX4324
NUMBER BUILT: approx. 12,680

Vought's "Corsair" family included the penultimate Goodyear F2G with its awesome R-4360 engine.

GOODYEAR F2G-1 *CORSAIR*

Vought's inimitable F4U *Corsair* will forever remain one of the great combat aircraft of all time. Not only was it credited with a kill/loss ratio of 11 to 1 against Japanese aircraft during World War II, it also was the last piston-engined fighter to be produced for the U.S. military. As a direct

Several F2Gs were used for racing after the war.

Aerofax, Inc. collection

Museum's F2G following its rediscovery at Norfolk.

result, it served actively in several foreign air forces until well into the late 1960s.

The *Corsair* came to life during 1938 in response to a U.S. Navy request calling for a new single-seat carrier-capable fighter. Vought's V-166B design, created by a team directed by Rex Beisel, generated considerable Navy interest, and during June of 1938, Vought received a contract to build and flight test a single prototype. This aircraft, when completed, sported a number of innovative features, not the least of which was an inverted "gull" wing which permitted substantial fuselage height while allowing the landing gear strut length to be kept at a minimum. All this had resulted from Beisel's desire to build the smallest airframe around the most powerful readily-available engine (the Pratt & Whitney XR-2800-4 radial). The power of the latter had dictated the use of a sizable propeller—which in turn required significant fuselage height for ground clearance.

The prototype *Corsair* flew for the first time on May 29, 1940, and quickly proved itself superior to virtually all other U.S. Navy (and in fact, all other U.S. military) aircraft. By the end of the year, it had achieved speeds in excess of 400 mph in level flight, and in every other performance arena it proved similarly impressive.

During June of 1941, the Navy placed its first firm order for production *Corsairs*, with deliveries taking place the following October. Initial operational experiences aboard aircraft carriers were not without significant difficulties, however, as pilots found the aircraft's exceptionally long nose and rearward cockpit placement to be a serious visual hindrance. Accordingly, initial entry of the

type into combat took place under the aegis of land-based Navy and Marine Corps units, with the type's first combat sorties being logged on February 13, 1943, at Bougainville.

Because of the priority placed on *Corsair* production during the early stages of World War II, several companies with requisite production facilities were utilized to increase delivery rates of the type to Navy and Marine Corps units. The two most important of these were the Brewster and Goodyear companies, which produced the F3A-1 and FG-1 versions of the F4U-1, respectively.

Nearly half of all *Corsairs* produced by these companies were delivered to the British and New Zealand military services. The British were, in fact, the first to utilize the *Corsair* during carrier operations, this event taking place on April 3, 1944, when *Corsairs* participated in the attacks on the German ship, *Tirpitz*. As a result of the success of these operations, new sea trials were ordered for the *Corsair* in the U.S. Navy service, and the result was approval of the type for carrier operations.

Miscellaneous versions of the *Corsair* followed the large number of F4U-1s to roll from Vought and Goodyear production lines, including the noteworthy F4U-2 night fighter, but it wasn't until the advent of the F4U-4 with its impressive 446 mph maximum speed, that new production contracts of any major significance were signed.

The end of the war brought with it serious cutbacks in military aircraft procurement. Though the *Corsair* was affected, production of the F4U-4 continued in order to meet anticipated U.S. Navy/U.S. Marine Corps and foreign ser-

vice needs. However, Goodyear production was terminated, and all other peripheral projects were either eliminated or brought back to Vought's home factory.

Termination of the Goodyear contract inadvertently led to the cancellation of two of the

Jay Miller/Aerofax, Inc.

The Museum's Goodyear F2G cockpit.

most ambitious of the many Vought *Corsair* versions, the F2G-1 and F2G-2. Starting with the F2G-1, these special *Corsairs* were optimized for low-altitude operations and were powered by the awesome Pratt & Whitney R-4360 twenty-eight cylinder four-row radial engine. The singular purpose of these special *Corsairs* was to overtake and destroy low-flying Japanese suicide ("Kamikaze") aircraft—which then were being observed in the Pacific Theatre in ever-increasing numbers.

The first of the R-4360 *Corsairs*, designated XF2G-1 and modified from a standard FG-1 airframe, was flight tested successfully during early 1944, and during March, the Navy awarded Goodyear a contract for 418 F2G-1s and 10 F2G-2s. The latter, unlike the former, was equipped for aircraft carrier operations and accordingly was equipped with folding wings and a tail hook. In production form, both types were given a bubble-type canopy to improve pilot vision during combat, and structural beef-ups were incorporated to accommodate the awesome power of the Pratt & Whitney engine. With a proposed water injection system, these aircraft were expected to achieve speeds in excess of 450 mph at the nominal altitude of 16,500 ft.

The advent of these aircraft came too late. With the cessation of hostilities, the five F2G-1s and five F2G-2s that had been completed ended the production run. Further contracts were immediately cancelled.

The standard *Corsair* armament package consisted of either six .50 cal. machine guns in the wings or four 20mm machine guns in the wings. Additionally, a wide variety of underwing stores could be attached to special wing hardpoints.

The Museum's F2G-1 was placed in a naval aircraft preservation can after tests in 1945, with only 246 hours of flying time. Rediscovered in the late 1960s by Captain Walt Ohlrich at Norfolk Naval Air Station, it was flown briefly but developed engine problems, and was landed at Patrick Henry Airport, Virginia.

The Marine Corps actually held title to the aircraft and claimed it for their Quantico museum. It was airlifted from Patrick Henry by an Army CH-64 and returned to Norfolk in 1974 when Champlin acquired title. Through the efforts of A&P Mechanic Jerry Devine of Philadelphia and pilot Dwain Trenton, the *Corsair* was readied and ferried to Enid, where it underwent a complete restoration.

The F2G is painted in its actual wartime colors, those of the Patuxent River Naval Air Test Center where it acquired all its military air and run time. The 454 on the fuselage denotes that this is the very first production F2G completed, Navy Bureau number 88454. It is the only flyable F2G variant in the world.

Champlin collection

The Museum's Goodyear F2G illustrating not only this version's huge R-4360 engine, but also its 360° vision bubble-type canopy.

DOUG'S COMMENTS:

Of the World War II aircraft on display, only one came from a government agency, and that was the F2G-1 *Corsair*. It's a roundabout story but illustrates the diverse nature of warbird acquisitions.

In 1974 I bought a Douglas *Dauntless* from Jack Tillman of Athena, Oregon. Jack had been trained as a Marine Corps pilot in World War II and wanted the SBD to go to the Marine Corps Museum in Quantico, Virginia but found no interest at that end. Consequently, he sold the historic Navy dive-bomber and I flew it only about a year before the Marines changed their mind. We arranged a straight-across trade: an AD-5 *Skyraider* and F2G-1 *Corsair* for the *Dauntless*.

Easier said than done. Navy Captain Walt Ohlrich had found the *Corsair* in a preservation container at Norfolk Naval Air Station in the early '60s and decided to fly it. But he had an engine failure, landing deadstick at nearby Patrick Henry Airport. However, by then the Marines caught onto the situation and realized the F2G officially belonged to them. Col. Tom D'Andrea

of the Quantico museum got the Army to transport the *Corsair* by helo to Norfolk in 1975, after which it went aboard the USS *Intrepid* (CV-11) museum in New York for the Bicentennial. Subsequently it was barged back to Norfolk, where I finally took delivery. I hired expert mechanic Jerry Devine to replace the engine—a job which required him to wear out two cars driving between Philadelphia and Norfolk. Thanks to Jerry and Dennis Buehn, the big Pratt and Whitney R-4360 was working again and my friend Dwain Trenton ferried the *Corsair* to Enid. He became highly proficient at airstarts along the way, as the engine quit every 10 or 15 minutes.

Too late for combat, the F2G series was limited to developmental testing at NAS Patuxent River, Maryland so our bird's total time is only about 250 hours. For the flight to Mesa I obtained the services of former Navy pilot and Thompson Trophy racer Ron Puckett.

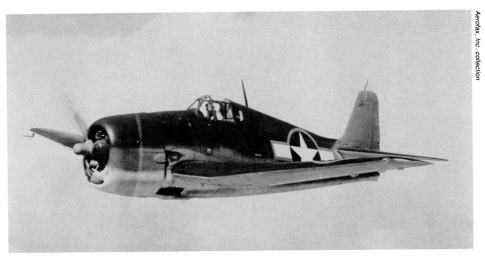

SPECIFICATIONS:

MANUFACTURER: Grumman Aircraft Corporation
DESIGNATION: F6F-3
FORMAL NAME: *Hellcat*
SERVICE/TYPE/NO. CREW: Navy carrier-borne fighter/single-seat
COUNTRY OF ORIGIN: U.S.A.
SERVED FROM/TO: 1942 through 1945
LENGTH: 33 ft. 7 in.
WINGSPAN/WING AREA: 42 ft. 10 in./ 334 sq. ft.
HEIGHT: 13 ft. 1 in.

EMPTY WEIGHT: 9,042 lbs.
GROSS WEIGHT: 11,381 lbs.
MAX. SPEED: 376 mph at 17,300 ft.
MAX. RANGE: 1,090 miles
MAX. ALTITUDE: 38,400 ft.
ENGINE MANUFACTURER: Pratt & Whitney
ENGINE DESIGNATION: R-2800-10
ENGINE TYPE: eighteen-cylinder air-cooled radial
POWER RATING: 2,000 hp
REGISTRATION/SERIAL NO.: NX103V
NUMBER BUILT: approx. 12,250

During WWII, the Grumman "Hellcat" became the most successful of all US Navy carrier-borne fighters.

GRUMMAN F6F-3 *HELLCAT*

The exigencies of war and the rapid development of a data base relating to enemy fighters frequently met in combat in the skies over Europe and the Pacific brought the U.S. Navy and the Grumman Aircraft Corporation to an expedited agreement concerning the need for a new fighter to supercede the Grumman F4F *Wildcat*. The resulting aircraft, ordered on June 30, 1941, was the XF6F-1 *Hellcat*—which was to become one of the most celebrated U.S. naval fighters of all time.

Following a series of developmental design changes during the course of hardware construction, the prototype *Hellcat*, as the XF6F-3, took to the air for the first time on June 26, 1942. Just over one month later, it was followed by the first production aircraft. By January of 1943,

Hellcats were on-hand with the first of many fleet operational squadrons, and consequently were moved aboard aircraft carriers for immediate service in combat zones. One-and-one-half years after the flight of the prototype, the *Hellcat*, on August 31, 1943, was in combat over Marcus Island.

A rapid escalation in the *Hellcat* production program at Grumman provided large quantities of the type for fleet service in a very short period of time. As a result, it was quick to replace the aging *Wildcat* as the Navy's single most important fighter, and in fact was to retain this title throughout the rest of the war.

Foreign use of the *Hellcat* was primarily British, and the type served admirably in the Fleet Air Arm from mid-1943 through the end of

the war. In British service, use was concentrated in the Far Eastern theatre. Night fighter versions of the *Hellcat* also were manufactured, the majority of these being equipped with pod-mounted radar units attached to the leading edge of the starboard wing.

Following the long production run of the original F6F-3 version, the F6F-5 came on line with the advantage of a slightly more powerful R-2800-10W engine, an improved engine cowl design, an updated windscreen and canopy configuration, improved ailerons, structurally redesigned tail surfaces, and additional armor plating for the pilot. Other improvements centered on the armament system.

At the end of the war, the *Hellcat* was credited with the destruction of 5,156 enemy aircraft. This figure included nearly three-quarters of all enemy aircraft destroyed in air-to-air combat.

After the war, the *Hellcat* soldiered on in a variety of roles, including drone and reconnaissance missions. Its last taste of combat occurred during the Korean War when several were modified as explosives-equipped drones and remotely controlled during flights from aircraft carriers to North Korean targets.

The standard *Hellcat* armament package consisted of either six .50 cal. machine guns in the wings, or two 20mm and four .50 cal. machine guns in the wings.

The Champlin Museum's *Hellcat* is the last F6F-3 variant in flying condition. It saw service and reserve duty until the early 1950s, including its brief use as a high-altitude photo aircraft. Champlin purchased the aircraft from Bill Ross in 1972.

DOUG'S COMMENTS:

Our F6F-3 is the third-oldest surviving *Hellcat*. It was offered by fellow collector Bill Ross of Chicago, who had introduced me to the warbird world. Bill's *Hellcat* had been a high-altitude photo bird in Georgia after disposal by the Navy, and I acquired it in 1974, logging a few hours before we grounded all our planes. Since the F6F produced more American aces than any other type, it is a particularly popular exhibit.

The Museum's Grumman F6F-3 cockpit.

The Museum's F6F-3 is thought to be the third oldest surviving "Hellcat". It is painted in authentic markings.

The Museum's "Hellcat" is the last F6F-3 in flyable condition and was utilized by the U.S. Navy Reserves until the early 1950s, when it was finally retired.

Lockheed

Lockheed's P-38 "Lightning" was built in many versions, including the double-canopy P-38M night fighter.

SPECIFICATIONS:

MANUFACTURER: Lockheed
DESIGNATION: P-38L
FORMAL NAME: *Lightning*
SERVICE/TYPE/NO. CREW: Army Air Corps fighter/single-seat
COUNTRY OF ORIGIN: U.S.A.
SERVED FROM/TO: 1941 through 1945
LENGTH: 37 ft. 10 in.
WINGSPAN/WING AREA: 52 ft. 0 in./ 327.5 sq. ft.
HEIGHT: 9 ft. 10 in.

EMPTY WEIGHT: 12,780 lbs.
GROSS WEIGHT: 21,600 lbs.
MAX. SPEED: 414 mph at 25,000 ft.
MAX. RANGE: 1,175 miles
MAX. ALTITUDE: 44,000 ft.
ENGINE MANUFACTURER: Allison
ENGINE DESIGNATION: V-1710-111/113 (F30)
ENGINE TYPE: twelve-cylinder liquid-cooled V
POWER RATING: 1,600 hp
REGISTRATION/SERIAL NO.: NL3JB/44-53097
NUMBER BUILT: approx. 9,900

LOCKHEED P-38L *LIGHTNING*

Originally conceived as a high-altitude interceptor to meet a 1937-vintage Air Corps requirement, Lockheed's Model 22 known as the P-38 *Lightning*, was to become one of the best-known U.S. fighters of World War II. The P-38 was Lockheed's first dedicated military aircraft and consequently, also was one of the earliest design projects to be associated with the name of Clarence L. "Kelly" Johnson (who later would become world-renowned for his efforts pertaining to the Lockheed F-104, U-2, and SR-71 programs; P-38 detail design was handled by Lockheed's H.L. Hibbard).

The most distinguishing feature of the *Lightning* was, of course, its podded fuselage and unusual twin-boom tail arrangement. Simply an innovative approach to the Air Corps specification, it later would prove ideal for the Pacific Theatre and the long, over-water flights it often required.

A prototype aircraft was ordered by the Air Corps on June 23, 1937, and as the XP-38, it made its first flight on January 27, 1939. An initial pre-production batch now was ordered, these being given more powerful Allison engines of 1,150 hp each, and a change in propeller rotation direction. Additionally, the armament configuration was upgraded and improved, and other minor changes were incorporated based on limited experience with the prototype.

Production of the type was moved ahead rapidly, in light of the threat of war, and by late 1940, over 500 *Lightnings* were on order. The initial run of P-38-designed aircraft now was replaced on the production line by the P-38D, and this series, with its self-sealing fuel tanks and changed horizontal tail incidence (to counter a buffet problem), was in turn superceded by the P-38E with its revised armament complement. Concurrent with P-38E production, some 660 non-supercharged versions were manufactured for the British.

These latter aircraft were never delivered and instead, were requisitioned by the Air Corps. The P-38F and P-38G series which now followed introduced more powerful engines, a modification called a "maneuvering flap" to improve maneuverability in combat, and other miscellaneous changes.

The P-38H, which was the last *Lightning* model to have early, faired radiators, represented the last of what some historians refer to as the first-generation "Lightnings". A second-generation series, distinguished by "chin"-type radiators aft and under the propeller spinners, was initiated with the introduction of the P-38J, which also had increased internal fuel and an associated endurance approaching a phenomenal 12 hours.

Perhaps the most important *Lightning* variant was the P-38L. Essentially a P-38J equipped with 1,600 hp engines, over 3,800 were manufactured.

The final noteworthy production *Lightning* version was the P-38M night fighter. This was one of the first radar-equipped fighters and was distinctive in having an elevated rear canopy transparency to accommodate a second seat for the observer.

Other P-38 versions, such as the F-4 and F-5, were optimized for reconnaissance and similar duties. An advanced *Lightning*, referred to as the XP-49 and equipped with a pressurized cockpit, also was built, along with the XP-58—which was a totally new and enlarged airframe to accommodate two crew members and a much heavier armament package.

The *Lightning* proved quite effective in com-

The Museum's Lockheed P-38L cockpit.

bat and was used in virtually every theatre of the war. Its great range and the psychological advantage of having two engines made it particularly attractive for use in Pacific operations. Numerous aces utilized the P-38 as their combat mount, the most notable being Capt. Richard Bong who eventually became the highest scoring U.S. ace of all time with 40 confirmed victories.

The standard *Lightning* armament package consisted of a combination of one 37mm or one 20mm machine gun and four .50 cal. machine guns, all mounted in the aircraft nose compartment. Additionally, a wide variety of underwing stores was possible, including bombs and rockets.

The Museum's P-38 was one of the very last produced, and was purchased by Champlin from Cecil Harp and Bob Ennis of Modesto, California and delivered to Mesa in 1983. The airplane was often seen at air shows in the 1970s. Champlin reconfigured the M back to more typical L layout, more appropriate to the 160 American aces who claimed five or more kills in the *Lightning*.

Jay Miller/Aerofax, Inc.

The Museum's Lockheed P-38L was one of the last "Lightnings" built and was modified from a P-38M night fighter to its present configuration.

Aerofax, Inc. collection

A Messerschmitt Bf 109E following a crash landing in England during the 1940 "Battle of Britain".

SPECIFICATIONS:

MANUFACTURER: Messerschmitt Flugzeubau (Hispano)
DESIGNATION: Bf 109E-3 (HA.1112M-1 Buchon)
FORMAL NAME: none
SERVICE/TYPE/NO. CREW: Luftwaffe fighter/single seat
COUNTRY OF ORIGIN: Germany
SERVED FROM/TO: 1935 through 1958
LENGTH: 28 ft. 4 in.
WINGSPAN/WING AREA: 32 ft. 4½ in./ 174 sq. ft.

HEIGHT: 7 ft. 5½ in.
EMPTY WEIGHT: 4,421 lbs.
GROSS WEIGHT: 5,523 lbs.
MAX. SPEED: 354 mph at 12,300 ft.
MAX. RANGE: 412 miles
MAX. ALTITUDE: 37,500 ft.
ENGINE MANUFACTURER: Daimler-Benz
ENGINE DESIGNATION: DB 601A
ENGINE TYPE: twelve-cylinder liquid-cooled V
POWER RATING: 1,100 hp
REGISTRATION/SERIAL NO.:
NUMBER BUILT:

MESSERSCHMITT Bf 109E-3

The Messerschmitt Bf 109 will forever rank among the world's most historically significant combat aircraft. Initial development work, under the aegis of the Bayerische Flugzeugwerke AG (Bf) and its chief designer, Willy Messerschmitt, was undertaken during 1934, and by the middle of the following year, in competition with several other manufacturers, the first aircraft, designated Bf 109a, was under construction. By early September it had been completed, and within weeks had taken to the air for the first time. During the course of the contract competition that followed, the Bf 109 proved superior to all but the aircraft submitted by the Heinkle team (the He 112). Further competition, the completion of several additional (improved) prototypes, and the realization that Messerschmitt and his design team had created a truly superior product, eventually eliminated the Heinkle aircraft as a serious contender.

During 1937, the Bf 109 was unveiled to the public for the first time at a Swiss air meet, and shortly afterwards, the type appeared in combat for the first time in the skies over Spain. In both arenas it proved completely successful, winning most of the Swiss competitions, and scoring kills against its Republican opponents without major difficulty in the Spanish Civil War.

Lessons learned in air combat led to a rapid development program. From the Bf 109B, Bf 109C, and Bf 109D, production switched to the first of the true production versions, the Bf 109E. Powered by an 1,100 hp Daimler-Benz engine and equipped with sufficient armament, it proved highly effective when used against Russian contemporaries. It was not until the middle of 1940,

when the first confrontations with the inimitable British Supermarine *Spitfire* took place, that the Bf 109 first met its match in combat.

Many sub-variants of the Bf 109E eventually reached the front, and this type became one of the dominant fighters of the war. It eventually was followed by the relatively limited production Bf 109F, and in turn, this model was followed by the more versatile Bf 109G. This aircraft basically was a Bf 109F series airframe with a 1,475 hp Daimler-Benz engine and very minor changes in the cowling (intakes) and small windscreen transparencies.

Numerous sub-variants of the Bf 109G eventually were produced before the end of the war, and this type eventually gained the reputation of being the best of the Bf 109 production models. Like its predecessors, it proved highly versatile, and was effective in ground support roles as well as air-to-air combat. Additionally, specialized versions served as reconnaissance system platforms, high-speed couriers, and bombers. Special two-seat trainers also were built, and many prototypes were developed to test items such as pressurized cockpits and high-altitude engines for operational versions.

The last recorded major Bf 109 operation of World War II occurred on April 7, 1945 when the Rammkommando Elbe unit attacked an incoming U.S. Air Force bomber raid. Of the 120 Bf 109s participating, only 15 returned safely.

The Bf 109 soldiered-on in several air forces following the end of the war. Most notably it continued in front-line service with the Spanish and Czechoslovakian air forces. With the former, it was manufactured in-country by Hispano under

the designation HA-1112; with the latter it was known as the Avia 109.

Armament packages available for the Bf 109 were greatly varied, but basically consisted of two to six MG 131 machine guns and/or two MG 151/20 machine guns and/or sometimes one or two MK 103 cannon. Underwing stores also were varied, with options including bombs and rockets.

It should be mentioned that the 33,500 Bf 109s estimated by most authoritative sources to have been built represents the largest semi-confirmable production figure for any aircraft in the world—with the possible exception of the Russian Polikarpov Po-2 (which some authorities claim has exceeded the 45,000 airframe mark).

Perhaps a dozen Messerschmitts remain in their German configuration, of which only the Daimler-Benz owned G variant and the Champlin Museum's are remotely capable of flight.

In 1972 Champlin began scouring the world for an intact, original German Bf 109 or, if necessary, a similar variant built elsewhere. Leads in Greece, the Near East and Europe were pursued without fruition.

In 1973 Champlin decided to purchase a postwar HA-1112 and reconfigure it to closely resemble the G-2 series upon which it was based. However, DB-605 engines and cowlings proved as elusive as original Messerschmitts. The airframe, already in the hand of Art Williams in Germany, was then adapted to the DB-601 engine and cowl, located in Switzerland.

This was an extensive job, involving fabricating new bearers and many other parts. The wings were reconfigured to the older

specification, and struts added to the tailplane. Interestingly, virtually the entire airframe is German-built, and most of the "Spanish" Messerschmitts in the U.S. also seem to be from the original batch of 25 Germany supplied to Spain in 1942-43. All instruments are German, and of the identifiable Spanish-built parts still on the aircraft, many, like the oil cooler, appear to

Jay Miller/Aerofax, Inc.

The Museum's Messerschmitt Bf 109E cockpit.

be identical to the German assemblies originally intended for the DB-601/605 engines.

Appropriate to the aircraft's cosmopolitan history, the cowling and engine are most likely from J392, the initial Dornier-Swiss built Messerschmitt Bf 109E supplied to Switzerland's *Flugwaffe*. J392 was accepted for Swiss service May 22, 1945, two weeks after the war ended in Europe.

The museum's aircraft is thus a "film personality", having appeared in both *Battle of Britain* and *Patton*. Parts of it have served in at least three continental air forces, yet it can all be traced back in a straight line to that angular little airplane first rolled from its Augsburg hangar in September 1935.

The Champlin Fighter Museum's Bf 109E-3 is displayed in 1940 *Battle of Britain* colors as flown by Hans "Assi" Hahn of *Jagdgeschwader Two Richthofen*.

The Museum's Bf 109E was built-up from parts of a Hispano HA.1112 and an original Bf 109E and is painted in authentic "Battle of Britain"-vintage markings.

North American's immortal "Mustang" originally was produced with a "razorback" canopy design.

Aerofax, Inc. collection

SPECIFICATIONS:

MANUFACTURER: North American Aviaiton
DESIGNATION: P-51D
FORMAL NAME: *Mustang*
SERVICE/TYPE/NO. CREW: Army Air Corps
fighter/single-seat
COUNTRY OF ORIGIN: U.S.A.
SERVED FROM/TO: 1942 through 1945
LENGTH: 32 ft. 3 in.
WINGSPAN/WING AREA: 37 ft. ¼ in./
233 sq. ft.
HEIGHT: 8 ft. 8 in.

EMPTY WEIGHT: 7,125 lbs.
GROSS WEIGHT: 12,100 lbs.
MAX. SPEED: 437 mph at 25,000 ft.
MAX. RANGE: 2,080 miles (ferry)
MAX. ALTITUDE: 41,900 ft.
ENGINE MANUFACTURER: Packard
ENGINE DESIGNATION: V-1650-7
ENGINE TYPE: twelve-cylinder liquid-cooled V
POWER RATING: 1,695 hp
REGISTRATION/SERIAL NO.: NL51X
NUMBER BUILT: approx. 15,680

NORTH AMERICAN P-51D *MUSTANG*

Any discussion concerning the single best combat aircraft of World War II would unquestionably center on North American's absolutely superb P-51 *Mustang*. Conceived during the first four months of 1940 in response to a combined Air Corps/Royal Air Force need for a high-performance pursuit suitable for utilization in the skies over Europe, it was flown for the first time on October 25 and immediately placed in production to meet British service needs.

Air Corps evaluation of two early production examples left the service with a favorable impression, but it was not ordered immediately. The Japanese attack on Pearl Harbor, several months after the evaluation, led to a reassessment of the first review, and within weeks, an initial production order was signed with North American. The latter, as it turned out, was for a ground attack version of the *Mustang* designated A-36.

The undeniably superior performance of the *Mustang* eventually led to a firm Air Corps order for the fully-equipped P-51A, and this aircraft, with the slightly more powerful Allison V-1710-81 engine, entered production during 1942. Conversion to the American-built version of the Rolls-Royce *Merlin* led to the P-51B and a significant improvement in performance and a redesign of the engine cowl. The P-51B proved popular enough to require the opening of a second production facility (in Grand Prairie, Texas), and P-51Cs were produced there. These differed insignificantly from the California-manufactured aircraft.

The arrival of P-51Bs in Britain during early December of 1943 was notable because it signified the appearance, for the first time, of a fighter that was capable of escorting bombers over virtually the entire distance to and from enemy territory. Accordingly, on January 15, 1944, just over a month after their first operational mission, they escorted Allied bombers to Germany and back.

While production of the P-51B/C continued, feedback from the various fronts was monitored with some intensity. Because of this, it was possible to note the regularity of complaints, one of which was the poor rearward view from the cockpit of the "razorback", first-generation *Mustangs*. The result of this was the first of the bubble canopy *Mustangs*, the P-51D. This aircraft, considered by many to be perhaps the definitive piston-engine fighter of World War II, was to be the most produced of all *Mustang* versions with nearly 8,000 being delivered.

The P-51D's great range, high maximum speed, and relatively docile flying characteristics made it popular wherever it was utilized. By 1944, it also was flying in the Pacific Theatre and on April 7, 1945, it was seen escorting Boeing B-29s over Tokyo for the first time.

Several lightweight testbeds eventually led to the last production *Mustang* version—the ultra-light and ultra-fast P-51H. This model, with its reduced weight and modestly improved aerodynamics, proved capable of achieving speeds of 487 mph in level flight—a feat not matched by any other production piston-engined fighter in the U.S.

The Korean War brought the *Mustang* back into combat following a five year hiatus. It proved quite effective in the ground support role, and though not capable of working one-on-one with state-of-the-art jets such as the MiG-15, nevertheless generated a significant air-to-air victory list.

The *Mustang's* success as a combat aircraft is one of the great aircraft stories of our time. It destroyed literally thousands of enemy aircraft in air-to-air combat, and thousands of tons of land and water-borne equipment in air-to-ground attacks, and until finally removed from the Air Force inventory during the early 1970s, it remained a highly competitive and effective combatant.

Armament varied considerably from version to version, but generally consisted of either four or six .50 cal. machine guns in wing mounts. Various external stores, including bombs and rockets, also were options.

"Ho Hun", permanently stabled in the museum, is owned and flown frequently by Bill Hane.

NL-151X was built in 1945 and served with the Air National Guard until surplussed in the late 50s. After three owners, Hane purchased the aircraft in 1981.

Jay Miller/Aerofax, Inc.

Bill Hane's North American P-51D cockpit.

The North American "Mustang" displayed in the Museum is owned and flown by Bill Hane and originally served with the Air Guard until being surplussed during the 1950s.

SPECIFICATIONS:

MANUFACTURER: Republic Aviation Corp.
DESIGNATION: P-47D
FORMAL NAME: *Thunderbolt*
SERVICE/TYPE/NO. CREW: Army Air Corps fighter/single-seat
COUNTRY OF ORIGIN: U.S.A.
SERVED FROM/TO: 1941 through 1945
LENGTH: 36 ft. 1¾ in.
WINGSPAN/WING AREA: 40 ft. 9 3/8 in./ 300 sq. ft.
HEIGHT: 14 ft. 7 in.

EMPTY WEIGHT: 10,000 lbs.
GROSS WEIGHT: 17,500 lbs.
MAX. SPEED: 426 mph at 30,000 ft.
MAX. RANGE: 1,800 miles
MAX. ALTITUDE: 42,000 ft.
ENGINE MANUFACTURER: Pratt & Whitney
ENGINE DESIGNATION: R-2800-59
ENGINE TYPE: eighteen-cylinder air-cooled radial
POWER RATING: 2,535 hp
REGISTRATION/SERIAL NO.: NX14519/42-8205
NUMBER BUILT: approx. 15,680

The Museum's rare "razorback" "Thunderbolt" was at one time a gate guardian at the La Paz, Bolivia airport.

REPUBLIC P-47D *THUNDERBOLT*

The final perturbation of a lengthy series of radial-engined fighters that included the P-35 and P-43, Republic's immense and powerful P-47 *Thunderbolt* was one of the truly great fighters of World War II. Designer Alexander Kartveli, after a series of early design studies that

Museum's P-47D in Bolivia with Bolivian markings.

"Thunderbolt" was heaviest US fighter of the war.

included several lightweight fighters with liquid-cooled engines, eventually settled on a radial-engined configuration with a gross weight of more than 12,000 lbs. At the time, this was the heaviest fighter ever ordered by the Air Force.

The prototype XP-47B took to the air for the first time on May 6, 1941, already having been ordered into production the preceding September. With its powerful 2,000 hp XR-2800 radial engine, it proved capable of speeds well in excess of 400 mph in level flight—a feat then matched in the U.S. only by the Vought *Corsair*.

The initial production *Thunderbolt* series was the P-47B and the first of these was delivered during mid-1942. The *Thunderbolt* was first flown in combat on April 8, 1943, and quickly proved itself to be rugged, reasonably fast, and outstanding in a dive. Its shortcomings surfaced, too, however, as it also lacked maneuverability, climb speed, and range.

The P-47C now was introduced on the production line, this version having a slightly longer fuselage and provisions for a centerline drop tank. It was followed, in turn, by the P-47D, which had water injection to increase engine power when needed, and wing pylons optimized for the transport of weapons and/or additional external fuel tanks.

The P-47D would, itself, undergo a major change midway through its production life when an experimental bubble canopy modification first applied to the one-off XP-47K was introduced on the *Thunderbolt* production line. This modifica-

tion permitted a dramatic improvement in pilot rearward vision and almost immediately became the standard configuration for all succeeding P-47s. Between the original 'razorback' P-47s and the newer bubble canopy versions, a total of 12,962 P-47Ds (including 354 P-47Gs built by Curtiss-Wright) were manufactured.

Following a miscellaneous collection of prototypes, the final full-production *Thunderbolt* model was the P-47N. Developed after an initial batch of YP-and P-47Ms with specially boosted 2,800 hp engines and maximum speeds of 470 mph, this version was optimized for great range and specifically for use in the Pacific Theatre. It differed from its predecessors in having a wing with increased span and increased internal fuel tankage, a more powerful engine, and numerous other lesser changes. Deliveries began during the spring of 1945, and the type served to escort Boeing B-29s during bombing missions for the rest of the war.

In combat, the *Thunderbolt* was an effective air-to-air fighter, but an even more effective ground support aircraft. Its great diving speed and ability to carry tremendous payloads made it ideal for air-to-ground work. Some 5,222 *Thunderbolts* were lost during the war, but only 3,499 of these were directly attributable to enemy action. Some 1,350,000 combat hours were flown with a combat loss rate per sortie of .7%.

The standard armament package found on the P-47 was eight .50 cal. machine guns in the

wings. Additionally, most *Thunderbolt* versions were capable of carrying a sizable external payload of bombs, rockets, and/or fuel tanks attached to wing hardpoints.

The *Thunderbolt* did not last long in American

The Museum's Republic P-47D cockpit.

postwar service, but served as late as 1966 in Latin America and elsewhere. The Museum's P-47D is a "reimport", once a gate guardian at La Paz, Bolivia Airport. Champlin acquired the plane from Jim Cullen in 1976, and shipped it off to Dick Martin of Carlsbad, California, who delivered the completed aircraft in 1981.

The aircraft is restored in the colors and markings of Colonel Robert L. Baseler, commanding officer, 325th Fighter Group, who designed the prominent "checker tail" marking which distinguished that group.

The Museum's "Thunderbolt" is immaculately restored and painted in the distinctive "checker tail" markings of the 325th Fighter Group during WWII.

SPECIFICATIONS:

MANUFACTURER: Vickers-Armstrong (Supermarine Division)
DESIGNATION: Mk.IX
FORMAL NAME: *Spitfire*
SERVICE/TYPE/NO. CREW: Royal Air Corps fighter/single-seat
COUNTRY OF ORIGIN: Great Britain
SERVED FROM/TO: 1937 through 1948
LENGTH: 31 ft. 4 in.
WINGSPAN/WING AREA: 32 ft. 7 in./ 231 sq. ft.
HEIGHT: 12 ft. 7¼ in.

EMPTY WEIGHT: 5,800 lbs.
GROSS WEIGHT: 7,500 lbs.
MAX. SPEED: 404 mph at 21,000 ft.
MAX. RANGE: 980 miles (ferry)
MAX. ALTITUDE: 42,500 ft.
ENGINE MANUFACTURER: Rolls-Royce
ENGINE DESIGNATION: "Merlin" 66
ENGINE TYPE: twelve-cylinder liquid-cooled V
POWER RATING: 1,720 hp
REGISTRATION/SERIAL NO.: MJ772/N8R
NUMBER BUILT: approx. 22,400

The Supermarine "Spitfire" is considered by most authorities to be Britain's most important WWII-vintage fighter.

SUPERMARINE *SPITFIRE* Mk.IX

Unquestionably the single most important British fighter of World War II, and not inconsequentially also one of the most important piston-engined fighters of all time, Supermarine's *Spitfire* came to life during the mid-1930s as a development of the company's successful late 1920s and early 1930s Schneider Trophy racers. A number of fighter-type design studies had resulted from these Schneider aircraft, but it wasn't until 1934 that R.J. Mitchell, Supermarine's chief engineer, created what he considered a definitive product.

The result of this work, in the form of the prototype *Spitfire* Mk.I, took to the air for the first time on March 5, 1936, and was an immediate success. Performance proved substantially superior to any operational combat aircraft then flying, and the Royal Air Force was impressed enough to immediately place an order for 310. By October of 1939, this figure had been increased to 4,000.

The first production *Spitfires* were delivered to the R.A.F. during June of 1938, and the following month, the type was assigned to its first operational squadron. Actual combat occurred for the first time during October of 1939, when *Spitfires* attacked fourteen Dornier Do 215s and Heinkel He 111s making a bombing run over the Firth of Fourth. The several victories scored by the new *Spitfires* became the first enemy aircraft to be destroyed over Great Britain since the end of World War I.

Spitfire production rates crept steadily upward during 1939 and early 1940 (the period of the "Battle of Britain"), and with them came a number of mechanical and technical improvements. The *Spitfire* Mk.II with increased engine power and a more versatile armament configuration followed the Mk.I, and the numerous variations in the Mk.II configuration effectively eliminated the Mk.III designator, while allowing the photo reconnaissance-configured Mk.IV to follow. The Mk.IV, in turn, was followed by the Mk.V with yet another increase in horsepower and the integration of no less than eight machine guns. This version was produced in many sub-variants, and as such, became the first to be used as a fighter-bomber and the first to be dispersed to overseas units.

The Mk.VIII was a knee-jerk reaction to the sudden appearance of the Focke-Wulf FW 190 in the skies over Europe and as such was given a significantly more powerful engine and other major changes. While it was being refined, an interim development utilizing the Mk.VC airframe became the Mk.IX. As this aircraft proved readily adaptable to production and was much needed by operational units, it by-passed the Mk.VIII and eventually became one of the most common and successful of all *Spitfire* versions. Following first deliveries of the *Spitfire* Mk.IX to front line squadrons during July of 1942, the type's first air-to-air victory was recorded on July 30 when a FW 190 was destroyed near Hornchurch. Over 5,700 *Spitfire* Mk.IXs eventually were built, making it the backbone of the R.A.F. throughout the most critical early years of the war.

Numerous other variants of the *Spitfire* were developed to handle specialized requirements, including high-altitude interception, and a lengthy series of prototypes were manufactured to study the attributes of improved armament systems, more powerful engines, pressurized cockpits, and a whole host of other options. Among the engine testbeds, however, was a single Mk.III which, when modified to fly with a Rolls-Royce *Griffon* engine, became the *Spitfire* Mk.XX. This aircraft set precedent for an entirely new family of *Spitfires* and as such, was the first of what became known as the Griffon *Spitfires* (until the advent of this aircraft, all production *Spitfires* had been powered by the Rolls-Royce Merlin engine).

Griffon-powered *Spitfires* proved to be the fastest, highest-flying, and hottest of all *Spitfires* produced. Speeds in excess of 450 mph were possible, and ceilings in excess of 42,000 ft. were common. The first production Griffon *Spitfire* was the Mk.XII which entered service during the spring of 1943. Performance of the Mk.XII was such that it was assigned the task, along with the Hawker *Tempest*, of intercepting and destroying German V-1 "buzz bombs". It quickly excelled in this role, and later recorded no less than 300 "buzz bomb" victories.

The next Griffon-powered *Spitfire* to enter production was the Mk.XIV, which had miscellaneous modifications to accommodate an engine that now was generating no less than 2,050 hp. Included in improvements found on this version was a distinctive five-bladed propeller, miscellaneous aerodynamic upgrades, and increased internal fuel capacity. The Mk.XIV proved to be a successful high-altitude fighter and on October 5, 1944, became the first Allied aircraft to destroy a German jet (a Messerschmitt Me 262).

The Mk.XIV was just being replaced on Supermarine production lines by the Mk.XVIII when the war came to an end. In turn, it was complemented in production by the Mk.XIX reconnaissance version.

The final production R.A.F. *Spitfires* were the Mks.XXI, XXII, and XXIV. These aircraft effectively were manufactured after the war was over, and differed from their predecessors in having

The Museum's Supermarine "Spitfire" Mk.IX cockpit.

upgraded wing designs, more powerful engines with, in some cases, six-bladed contra-rotating propellers, and other major modifications. These, along with their Royal Navy counterparts, were to be the last *Spitfires* in production, rolling from Supermarine factories during 1947—some two years after the war had ended.

Royal Navy use of the *Spitfire* under the name *Seafire* also had proven substantial, with over 2,000 eventually being manufactured specifically for that service. Virtually every R.A.F. version of the *Spitfire* was mirrored in an R.N.A.S. version, with the majority of the differences being visible in the form of strengthened landing gear, the addition of an arresting hook, folding wings, and other dedicated naval peculiarities.

The *Spitfire's* accomplishments during World War II were legion. Numerous aces, including Douglas Bader, Robert Stanford-Tuck, and John nie Johnson, to name just a few, utilized the *Spitfire's* services in combat, and several thousand German and Italian aircraft fell to its guns. Pilots invariably appreciated its sensitive controls, its throttle response, and its maneuverability, but fault was found in its relatively short range, and susceptibility to enemy fire.

During the course of its life, the *Spitfire* was to see a weight growth of 40%, a speed increase of 35%, a rate-of-climb increase of 80%, and an engine power increase of 100%. All of these were the direct result of war requirements, which in turn were generated by the perceived performance improvements noted in enemy aircraft.

Armament packages were numerous and highly variable. Generally speaking, however, the .303 machine gun and/or the .20mm machine gun was standard, and often grouped in counts of eight with mixes of each type possible. Late model *Spitfires* sometimes were equipped with two .50 cal. machine guns. Additionally, select models could carry bombs or rockets mounted on underwing attachment points.

MJ772 actually saw combat. Manufactured in late 1943, the airplane was in service with Free French No. 341 Squadron at Biggin Hill. No. 341 and at least fifty-four other *Spitfire* units supported the June 1944 Normandy Invasion. Their mission was to expedite the breakout from the beachhead when MJ772 sustained battle damage and was out of service for four days. It returned to direct air support missions on June 22, markings changed from code letters NL to GW to reflect a new unit assignment with No. 340 Squadron—341's sister unit from the Biggin Hill days.

In early August 1944, MJ772 was withdrawn from combat and shifted to several maintenance and support units. When flown in January 1945 it was damaged and made further rounds of support and repair units. Eventually Vickers-

Champlin collection

The Museum's Supermarine "Spitfire" underwent a five-year restoration program following a landing mishap in Amarillo, Texas.

support and repair units. Eventually Vickers-Armstrong reacquired MJ772 and five other Mk.IXs for conversion to two-seat training aircraft for Ireland. This group was delivered in June 1951. When MJ772 was retired from Irish service in January 1960 her logbook showed 1,402 hours.

But that was not the end of flying and fame for MJ772. In fact, she was to see the smoke and flames of battle again, this time the special-effects fires of the 1968 film *The Battle of Britain*. From August 1967 Film Aviation Services used her as one of the primary camera and background aircraft, until W.C. "Connie" Edwards bellyed her in July 9, 1968.

Champlin acquired the aircraft from W.J.D. Roberts, who had flown and displayed it at the Strathallan Museum in Scotland. Registered N8R in December 1974, she ground-looped under ferry to Arizona in July 1980, initiating a five-year restoration and conversion back to original single-seat configuration and markings. The result is the splendid ca. 1944 aircraft now on display.

"Boots" Blesse checking six by Jack Fellows.

The photos and information in this section of the book pertain to the aircraft currently on display in the Champlin Fighter Museum. We have attempted also to integrate material relating to the gun systems carried by these aircraft wherever such items relate to our gun collection.

POST-WAR JETS

SPECIFICATIONS:

MANUFACTURER: McDonnell Aircraft Co.
DESIGNATION: F-4N
FORMAL NAME: *Phantom II*
SERVICE/TYPE/NO. CREW: Navy carrier-borne fighter/fighter-bomber/two-seat
COUNTRY OF ORIGIN: U.S.A.
SERVED FROM/TO: 1958 through 1974
LENGTH: 58 ft. 3¾ in.
WINGSPAN/WING AREA: 38 ft. 4 7/8 in./ 530 sq. ft.
HEIGHT: 16 ft. 3 in.
EMPTY WEIGHT: 28,000 lbs.

GROSS WEIGHT: 54,600 lbs.
MAX. SPEED: 1,485 mph
MAX. RANGE: 2,300 miles (ferry condition)
MAX. ALTITUDE: 62,000 ft.
ENGINE MANUFACTURER: General Electric
ENGINE DESIGNATION: J79-GE-8
ENGINE TYPE: turbojet
POWER RATING: 17,000 lbs. th. a-b; 10,900 lbs. th. mil.
REGISTRATION/SERIAL NO.: Bu No. 153016
NUMBER BUILT: approx. 5,200

McDonnell's F-4 "Phantom II" was built for the Air Force, Marines, Navy, and a number of foreign customers.

McDONNELL F-4N *PHANTOM II*

Future aerospace historians almost certainly will look back on the ubiquitous McDonnell F-4 *Phantom II* as perhaps the most successful and versatile jet fighter of the twentieth century. Starting life during 1954 as a study calling for a marginally transonic ground attack aircraft to be designated AH-1, and eventually reaching the hardware stage during 1958 as the Mach 2

capable F4H-1 prototype interceptor, it took to the air for the first time on May 27, 1958.

Following a fly-off against the superb Vought F8U-3, the *Phantom II* was selected by the Navy to meet its forthcoming fighter and fighter-bomber requirements, and an initial batch of F-4As (initially F4H-1Fs—but this designation was changed to F-4A during 1962) was immediately ordered. These were followed by more-definitive F-4Bs and the first of the reconnaissance versions, the RF-4B.

Air Force interest in the aircraft's superb capabilities now led to an order for their first *Phantom IIs* as F-110s. These aircraft basically were F-4Bs with specialized Navy equipment removed and Air Force gear added. By the time this version began to enter the Air Force inventory, its designation had been changed to the more uniform F-4C. A reconnaissance version, referred to as the RF-4C, also went into production not long after the F-4C entered service.

By the mid-1960s, nearly thirty Navy squadrons were operating the F-4B. U.S. involvement in Vietnam caused the type to be used operationally almost from the very beginning of its service career, and though optimized initially for the interceptor role, it soon became the Navy's workhorse striker aircraft. In the ground support role, it proved itself a capable transport of bombs and other ground attack weapons, and literally thousands of tons were delivered on targets until the U.S. departed Vietnam during the mid-1970s.

F-4B production was followed by the F-4J which offered an improved bombing system, an upgraded radar, a data link system, upgraded

The Museum's McDonnell F-4N front cockpit.

engines, and larger wheels and tires to increase permissible landing weight.

During January of 1971, a Navy upgrade program codenamed "Project Bee-line", was undertaken to modify and upgrade a total of 178 older F-4Bs as an interim measure until the introduction of the Grumman F-14A *Tomcat*. Following the modification process, these aircraft were referred to a F-4Ns and had strengthened structures, improved bombing systems, data link, an upgraded identification-friend-or-foe system, a dogfighting computer, and numerous other changes and improvements. "Project Bee-line" lasted from February of 1973 to late 1975.

Aside from miscellaneous testbeds and a series of QF-4B drones, the last of the many Navy *Phantom II* versions was the F-4S, which was the F-4J version run through a program similar to "Project Bee-line". It also had leading-edge high-lift devices added to the wings and tail surfaces in order to improve maneuverability characteristics.

Air Force use of the F-4 was perhaps even more ubiquitous than the Navy, even in consideration of the fact that the type had begun life as a Navy product. Following the initial F-4C production run, the Air Force acquired the F-4D during 1965, which was a refined version of its predecessor with improved weapon systems and slightly less fuel capacity. In turn, this version was followed by the definitive F-4E, which carried a much-needed fixed, forward firing M-61 rotary-type machine gun in its elongated nose. Coupled with numerous other improvements and system upgrades, this dedicated fighter *Phantom II* proved a deadly combatant when utilized

in the skies over Vietnam.

Foreign use of the F-4 was, and remains, quite widespread. Numerous countries include the type in their respective inventories, and some, such as Israel, can claim aces who earned virtually all their victories while flying *Phantom IIs* in combat.

Armament packages found on the various

The Museum's McDonnell F-4N rear cockpit.

F-4s were quite variable. Generally, however, the standard Navy configuration consisted of four AIM-7 *Sparrow* radar-guided air-to-air missiles and up to four AIM-9 *Sidewinder* infrared-guided air-to-air missiles. Additionally, several different gun pod options were available for wing or centerline attachment. Wing pylons could accept an incredible variety of ordnance that included up to 16,000 lbs. of bombs, rockets, or whatever else was required.

The Museum's F-4N is a rebuilt F-4B. This aircraft is a genuine combat veteran of many missions with VF-21 aboard USS *Ranger*. After the war, it served with VF-301, a Naval Reserve Squadron. Jack Hayes, Vietnam vet and pilot, rescued the big fighter from the boneyard in 1983 and, with 123 volunteers, had restored it by June of 1984. These are its actual 1968 markings, though the names on the canopy sills reflect four Navy fliers killed in Vietnam flying off *Ranger*—LT Larry Lewis and his RIO, LTJG Tony Miller are painted port while LT Jim Duensing and LTJG Roy Haviland are on starboard.

The Museum's F-4N flew many missions over Vietnam while assigned to VF-21 aboard the US Navy carrier USS "Ranger". After Vietnam, it was assigned to VF-301.

Aeroflax, Inc. collection

The MiG-17 has equipped the front line units (including those of Czechoslovakia, shown) of over thirty air forces.

SPECIFICATIONS:

MANUFACTURER: Mikoyan, A.I. and Gurevich, M.I. and Soviet state factories
DESIGNATION: MiG-17
FORMAL NAME: *Fresco* (NATO codename)
SERVICE/TYPE/NO. CREW: Frontal Aviation fighter/single-seat
COUNTRY OF ORIGIN: Soviet Union, et.al.
SERVED FROM/TO: 1950s through 1960s
LENGTH: 36 ft. 4½ in.
WINGSPAN/WING AREA: 31 ft. 7 in./ 243.3 sq.ft.
HEIGHT: 12 ft. 5 5/8 in.

EMPTY WEIGHT: 8,200 lbs. (approx.)
GROSS WEIGHT: 13,380 lbs.
MAX. SPEED: 711 mph at 9,840 ft.
MAX. RANGE: 1,397 miles
MAX. ALTITUDE: 54,460 ft.
ENGINE MANUFACTURER: Klimov
ENGINE DESIGNATION: VK-1
ENGINE TYPE: turbojet
POWER RATING: 5,950 lbs. to 7,495 lbs. of thrust
REGISTRATION/SERIAL NO.: 1FJ-10 (Morroco)/1406016
NUMBER BUILT: approx. 9,000

MIKOYAN MiG-17

Developed by the Mikoyan and Gurevich design bureau, the MiG-17 was an expected evolutionary development of its MiG-15 predecessor. Though not as well known as the MiG-15, eventualy it was manufactured in similar numbers over a production life spanning from 1950 through early 1957.

Following prototyping and the end of state trials during 1952, the MiG-17 entered the operational Soviet air force inventory as a complement to the MiG-15. Because it was equipped with the powerful VK-1A turbojet engine found in MiG-15bis version, its performance was exceptional. The latter was, in fact, enhanced by the MiG-17's almost totally new wing design. This employed a thinner wing section, a greater sweep angle (it actually was swept in two sections with the inboard section at 43° and the outboard section at 47°), and other changes.

Fuselage differences were minimal, with the empennage section being stretched to accommodate a longer exhaust pipe, and later an afterburner, and the airbrakes were redesigned and enlarged. Other changes noted were slightly revised horizontal and vertical tail surfaces, cockpit upgrades (including an improved ejection seat), and the addition of a ventral fin (for improved high-speed and high angle-of-attack directional stability).

A number of different production versions of the MiG-17 were identified by NATO observers during the course of the type's service life. Some, for instance, were equipped with a combination bullet/lip-type radar installation in the intake; some had repositioned airbrake installations; some had revised windscreen configurations to accommodate cockpit equipment changes; and some special Polish-manufactured models were equipped with thickened wing root sections to provide aerodynamic fairings for special dual-wheel main landing gear and a drag-chute (permitting rough field utilization). Each of these was assigned a specific letter following the formal *Fresco* NATO code name (i.e., *Fresco-A, Fresco-B,* etc.).

The MiG-17 saw combat during the Korean War and Vietnam, and since has been utilized in a number of other conflicts around the world. Perhaps the most notable of the latter are those that have occurred in the Middle East.

Numerous "third-world" countries have found the MiG-17 to their liking, and reports available to western sources indicate it is easy to fly, distinctly simple to maintain and operate, and relatively inexpensive to own and maintain. At least twenty countires either still have it on inventory, or have had it on inventory in the past.

Armament packages included two to three

Jay Miller/Aeroflax, Inc.

The Museum's MiG-17 now is painted in N. Vietnamese AF markings.

Champlin collection

Arrival of the Museum's MiG-17 via "Hercules".

Champlin collection

Shipment of the MiG-17 was completed by flatbed.

Jay Miller/Aeroflax, Inc.

The Museum's MiG-17 cockpit.

NR-23 23mm cannon in the nose or up to four early-version *Alkali* radar-guided air-to-air missiles. Additionally, external mounting of rocket pods and bombs was possible under the wings.

The Museum's aircraft is an early production version formerly active with the Moroccan Air Force, and brought here through the efforts of Major General "Boots" Blesse, former President of the American Fighter Aces Association, and Colonel Major Kabbaj, Royal Moroccan Air Force. The transfer to the Champlin Museum was approved by His Highness King Hassan II in 1983.

The Museum's MiG-17 in the Moroccan Air Force color scheme it was in when delivered to the Museum. It since has been painted in a North Vietnamese Air Force scheme.

Aerofax, Inc. collection

Many North American "Sabrejets" have been used for test and drone work.

SPECIFICATIONS:

MANUFACTURER: North American Aviation
DESIGNATION: F-86F
FORMAL NAME: *Sabrejet*
SERVICE/TYPE/NO. CREW: Air Force fighter/ single-seat
COUNTRY OF ORIGIN: U.S.A.
SERVED FROM/TO: 1947 through 1961
LENGTH: 37 ft. 6½ in.
WINGSPAN/WING AREA: 37 ft. 1 in./ 288 sq. ft.
HEIGHT: 14 ft. 8 in.
EMPTY WEIGHT: 10,857 lbs.

GROSS WEIGHT: 20,324 lbs.
MAX. SPEED: 608 mph at sea level
MAX. RANGE: 1,615 miles (ferry)
MAX. ALTITUDE: 48,000 ft.
ENGINE MANUFACTURER: General Electric
ENGINE DESIGNATION: J47-GE-27
ENGINE TYPE: turbojet
POWER RATING: 4,320 lbs. th. normal/ 5,200 lbs. th. maximum
REGISTRATION/SERIAL NO.: 51-13371
NUMBER BUILT: approx. 6,860

NORTH AMERICAN F-86F *SABRE*

Based on development work then underway on the Navy's forthcoming North American FJ-1 *Fury* jet fighter of 1944, the Air Force moved ahead, during the autumn of 1944, with a project calling for the development of a similar jet fighter under the designation XP-86. This aircraft initially was to have been configured with straight wings, but following the discovery of German studies pertaining to the attributes of swept wings, the

Champlin collection

Museum's F-86F is on loan from the USAF Museum.

Champlin collection

Museum's F-86F had served with the S. Korean A.F.

latter were integrated into its design.

The prototype XP-86 was completed during mid-1947 and flown for the first time on October 1. Given a wing with a sweep angle of 35°, innovative wing high-lift devices, boosted controls, a pressurized cockpit, and other then-advanced features, it was one of the most sophisticated fighters in the world at the time of its debut.

Production contracts for P-86As followed immediately on the heels of the prototype's first flight, and during June, the designation formally was changed from P-86 to F-86 in acknowledgement of the Air Force's new "fighter" category (replacing the old "pursuit" category).

Following the establishment of a 670.981 mph clocking during a formal speed run on September 15, 1948, the F-86 became officially the fastest aircraft in the world. By the end of 1949, two full fighter groups were *Sabre* equipped.

The initial production run of F-86As soon was replaced by the significantly improved F-86E (no F-86Bs were built; the proposed F-86C, with NACA-type flush intakes was redesignated YF-93A—only two were built for test purposes) which offered all-moving horizontal tail surfaces, boosted tail surface controls, and artificial feel for the pilot. This version, in turn, was complemented in production (on another line) by the F-86F which offered a new wing leading edge and small boundary layer fences. Additionally, and perhaps most importantly, it was equipped with the more powerful 5,970 lb. thrust General Electric J 47GE-27 turbojet engine.

Deliveries of the F-86F, with its improved high-altitude performance (stemming from the new

wing and more powerful engine) were initiated during late March of 1952. By the end of the year, it was in combat over Korea. The modifications proved sufficient to keep the aircraft competitive with the newer MiG models that were also beginning to appear, and production continued until long after the Korean War had ended. An F-86F, in fact, eventually became the last *Sabre* to be delivered, this taking place during December of 1956.

Radar-equipped *Sabres* were unveiled in the form of the F-86D version which first was flown on December 22, 1949. Equipped with an afterburner and an advanced weapon system, the *Sabre Dog*, as it was nicknamed, proved only nominally effective in the all-weather intercepter role, and subsequently, most of those built were upgraded to F-86Ls. As such, they were given a 2 ft. increase in wing span (similar to that found on the F-86H), slotted leading edges, and a data link providing integration with a ground controlled intercept system.

Another radar equipped version, the F-86K, was developed for sale to foreign countries. Eventually, a number of these were acquired by European air forces with the majority being manufactured in Italy.

Though not the last F-86 version to be manufactured (that honor going to the F-86F), the F-86H was perhaps the most capable. Equipped with an 8,929 lb. thrust General Electric J73-GE-3 engine, it had a greater wingspan, a longer and deeper fuselage, strengthened landing gear, revised horizontal tail surfaces, and an improved armament complement. The added thrust of the engine made this the fastest

production *Sabre*, and its other design features made it one of the most capable in air-to-air combat.

The *Sabre* first arrived in Korea during December of 1950, almost exactly one month following the first sighting of the MiG-15. These two combatants met for the first time on December 17, with the F-86A scoring four kills

Jay Miller/Aerofax, Inc.

The Museum's North American F-86F cockpit.

against no losses. This and several later skirmishes between the two swept-wing adversaries revealed that though the two aircraft were closely matched, the MiG-15 had the better rate of climb and better high-altitude performance; concommitantly, it suffered from inferior maneuverability at low altitude, control anomalies that could prove fatal in certain parts of the flight envelope, and poor piloting technique.

Post-Korean War use of the *Sabre* was extensive, and various air forces around the world eventually bought *Sabres* to serve in a variety of roles, including interceptor, bomber, and photo-reconnaissance. The *Sabre* remains in service to this very day, though only in very limited numbers. It is utilized by the U.S. military as a drone, and a few third-world countries still maintain it on strength, primarily for use as a fighter-trainer.

Armament packages normally consisted of up to six fuselage-mounted .50 cal. machine guns and a combination of externally mounted bombs or air-to-surface rockets. Rocket packs were mounted in the under-nose areas of radar-equipped *Sabres* and were optimized for air-to-air combat.

The Museum aircraft is on long term loan from the Air Force, and is displayed in the markings of then-Major Blesse's *Sabre*, flown with the Fourth Fighter Wing in 1952. The Fourth Wing was the first to operate *Sabres* in the Korean War, joining combat operations December 17, 1950.

Champlin collection

Following removal of its Korean Air Force camouflage, it was decided that the "Sabrejet" should be displayed in the Korean War-vintage markings of the 4th Fighter Wing.

The Grumman "Hellcat" was powered by the Pratt & Whitney R-2800 air-cooled radial engine.

The Museum's Fokker Dr.I recently has been reengined with an authentic rotary.

The rapid and successful development of lightweight aircraft propulsion systems is probably the single most important hardware event in the history of aviation. The virtual non-existence of engines with power-to-weight ratios suitable for flight unquestionably was the largest stumbling block faced by early aviation pioneers. Accordingly, most not only were challenged to design and build their own aircraft, but also the engines to power them as well.

Definitive studies during the early 1800s by Sir George Cayley—determining that human muscle power was generally insufficient for practical aero-propulsion—earlier had laid the groundwork for a concerted effort to develop engines applicable to heavier-than-air flight. Seminal work in the field of steam powerplants initially appeared promising, but eventually, weight considerations that were the end product of metallurgical constraints, dictated exploration of other internal combustion engine forms. Accordingly, during 1889, an Australian by the name of Lawrence Hargrave built and tested perhaps the world's first three-cylinder rotary

(powered by compressed air), thus unwittingly setting precedent for a powerplant design that would become a standard for the majority of the aircraft flown during the first few years of World War I. This engine, wherein the cylinders, pistons, and attached propeller rotated around a fixed crankshaft, had the attribute of being light, relatively powerful, and self-cooling.

By 1900, the development of early radial engines, wherein the cylinders and crankcase were rigidly attached to the aircraft firewall but the crankshaft and its attached propeller were not, had proved them to be eminently more practical. It was discovered they provided considerably more horsepower per pound of weight, and perhaps most importantly, unlike the rotary, they did not impart a gyroscopic element into the control and stability dynamics of the aircraft itself.

During 1898, Charles Manley, a skilled engineer with a strong background in engine design and related disciplines, joined forces with the director of the Smithsonian Institution, Dr. Samuel Langley, in an attempt to design, build,

An Austro Daimler six-cylinder powered the Aviatik.

The Sopwith "Pup" had a LeRhone 9.

Fw-190D-13's Junkers Juno 213 was run-up following completion of restoration process during late 1989.

THE AIRCRAFT COLLECTION
ENGINES

and test-fly the world's first practical aircraft. Though the project eventually resulted in the completion of a technically viable machine, two unsuccessful attempts to fly during 1903 resulted in failure, and the project was abandoned. Nevertheless, the Balzer-Manley engine developed for this aircraft was unquestionably the most advanced in the world at the time of its debut and was capable of producing no less than 52.4 hp at a gross weight of less than 200 lbs. This power-to-weight ratio was not bettered significantly until near the end of World War I.

Shortly after the failure of the Langley/Manley aircraft, Orville Wright literally flew into history when he and his "Wright Flyer" became airborne over the sand dunes of Kitty Hawk, N. Carolina on December 17, 1903. The engine developed for the Flyer was a small, water-cooled in-line four-cylinder. It produced approximately 16 horsepower against a total weight of 180 lbs.

Between the time of the Langley-Manley/ Wright Brothers experiments and the outbreak of World War I during 1914, progress in the development of aircraft propulsion systems was enormous. Of greatest importance was a rapid transition away from "home-built" engines and toward factory-manufactured and mass-produced engines, with the latter offering considerably greater reliability and efficiency. Concurrent with this trend was the birth of what was soon to become the most famous aircraft engine of its day, the Gnome rotary.

During the first decade of the 20th century, France had ascended to become the premier manufacturer of automobile racing engines. Among its stellar designers were the brothers Louis and Laurent Seguin who began during 1907 to work on a rotary engine modelled after the Lawrence Hargrave design of nearly a quarter-century earlier. By 1908, a five-cylinder engine, producing some 34 hp and weighing only about 112 lbs., was in test.

Word of this engine's light weight, dependability, and high horsepower spread quickly throughout the fledgling French aviation community, and by the end of the decade, it was unquestionably the powerplant of choice. With the outbreak of World War I during 1914, the rotary's ready availability pushed it to the forefront of production quotas and until more advanced propulsion systems became available during 1917, thousands upon thousands were manufactured by all combatants in a wide variety of designs and horsepower ratings.

The rotary design was noteworthy not only because of its timely attributes, but also because of its somewhat quirky failings. Castor oil, because of the necessity that it be mixable with gasoline, was the lubrication of choice and copious quantities were required. Because it was involved in the combustion process, the lubricating medium was ejected as a mist through the exhaust vents, and both crew members and aircraft were invariable covered with a castor oil film following a flight. Additionally, rotaries were notorious for shedding cylinders in flight, and the sudden assymmetry of the rotating mass was usually catastrophic for both crew and aircraft. Perhaps most chronic was the difficulty pilots had in throttling. The rotary's basic design was not highly conducive to an effective fuel control system, and as a result, power was not highly variable and the accepted means of retarding an engine was by "blipping" the spark plugs. The latter involved killing electrical power to one or several spark plugs in concert, this effectively cutting power for landing or taxi requirements.

Unfortunately for the Gnome engine, newly-arrived non-rotary designs quickly proved to be significantly more efficient and capable of producing considerably more horsepower. Though somewhat heavier than their rotary stablemates, liquid-cooled straight and V-type engines by 1917 had moved into the forefront of aircraft engine technology and had exposed the rotary's significant failings. Engines of four, six, eight, twelve, and even fourteen cylinders were generating up to 400 hp by the end of the war, and as a result, rotary designs faded from prominence and only a very few remained in production by the beginning of 1918.

While German manufacturers concentrated on the design of "straight-six" liquid-cooled engines during the remaining months of the war, work

The Allison V-1710 was the most popular US-manufactured liquid-cooled engine of WWII.

A nine-cylinder Clerget is one of several WWI-vintage air-cooled rotary engines owned by the Museum.

already had begun in the U.S. and Great Britain on production V-type engines of twelve cylinders and 400 hp. Resulting from this multi-thrust effort were several of the most significant aircraft powerplants of their day, including Britain's Rolls Royce *Falcon* and *Eagle*, and the U.S. consortium-designed *Liberty*. The latter, offering 1 hp for every 2.1 lbs. of weight, was the most efficient production engine in the world at the time of its debut, and much the preferred powerplant for larger aircraft types.

While work on V-type liquid-cooled engines had progressed rapidly during the latter stages of World War I, the air-cooled radial also had been considerably improved. Difficulties stemming from metallurgical and cooling anomalies had delayed this engine type's ascendency, but with the development of efficient baffling systems and steadily reduced cross-sectional areas, its attributes soon moved it into even contention with its liquid-cooled siblings.

The between-war period of 1920 through approximately 1940 saw considerable improvement in the design of both liquid-and air-cooled designs. British development of such notable radials as the Bristol *Jupiter* and Armstrong Siddeley *Jaguar*—both capable of producing some 500 hp—made them the preferred fighter engine of their day, and the somewhat earlier successes enjoyed by the Wright Whirlwind when installed in Charles Lindbergh's immortal Spirit of St. Louis helped catapult the Wright and Pratt & Whitney companies into the forefront of engine manufacturers in the U.S.

Perhaps the most important technological engine development during this period was the successful integration of the mechanical and turbo-supercharger. This device, either through mechanical means or via the power contained in an engine's exhaust gases, forced oxygen-laden air into a cylinder at high altitude. Because the air pressure at 20,000 ft. was only half that at sea level, engine efficiency effectively deteriorated with increasing altitude, and superchargers were required to ensure that sufficient oxygen was available for combustion processes to take place.

Though radial engines had begun to take over as the dominant aircraft powerplant, liquid-cooled engines continued to be developed with no less vigor. Due to their innately lower frontal area, they also tended to be the powerplant of choice for fighters and similar high-performance aircraft. Speed and altitude records now were being broken with significant regularity and by the mid-1930s, aircraft had exceeded 400 mph in level flight and achieved altitudes in excess of 50,000 ft. These performances, unfortunately, also represented a plateau, of sorts, for propeller-driven machines. Horsepower and aerodynamic concerns now had begun to dictate

limits to just how fast and how high an aircraft could go, and it was becoming increasingly apparent that for further improvement to take place, new forms of propulsion would have to be developed.

Jet propulsion, contrary to popular belief, even during the 1930s, was far from being a totally new concept. As early as 1791, patents for gas turbines had been issued in Great Britain, and during the 1800s, considerable interest was expressed in the utilization of gas turbines for power production. During 1910, Henri Coanda, a French-Canadian, proposed the use of a gas turbine in an aircraft (a prototype apparently was built and unsuccessfully tested), and during the 1920s, studies calling for the development of an early form of turboprop engine were completed by noted engineers H. H. Constant and A. A. Griffith.

Partly as a consequence of these long-standing interests, Frank Whittle, then a cadet at Cranwell College in England, began pursuing the idea of creating what came to be known as the turbojet engine. During 1928, he completed work on his term thesis at the Royal Air Force College describing what he considered to be "probable future developments in aircraft design", and in this paper, he outlined the basic concept of the jet engine wherein hot gases produced internally and expelled aft would generate physical thrust sufficient to propel an aircraft forward at a high rate of speed. The beauty of his proposal was that there appeared to be virtually nothing to limit forward velocity except aerodynamics and structure.

Though little initial interest in Whittle's jet engine was expressed by the Royal Air Force and the British aircraft engine community, he refused to give up. During January of 1930, his design was granted a patent, and for the following five years, he explored financing options while slowly assembling a small group of influential supporters. During March of 1936, Whittle and several backers created Power Jets Ltd., and with L2,000 as seed money, began the design and construction of the world's first turbojet engine. The first successful run was completed on April 12, 1937, and some four years later, a much-refined version of this engine powered the Gloster E.28/39 during the first flight by an Allied jet-propelled aircraft.

Though the first off the mark with a patent and actual hardware, Whittle was not the only engineer interested in jet propulsion. In Germany, Pabst von Ohain and several associates had moved ahead with jet engine designs of their own, and with significant government support, had succeeded in rapidly developing an aircraft-worthy powerplant that in fact was used to propel the Heinkel He 178 into the air on August 27, 1939, on what was the first turbojet aircraft flight

The General Electric J79 was one of the world's first truly successful Mach 2-capable turbojet engines.

General Electric J47 was used in a number of US combat aircraft, including the "Sabrejet" and "Stratojet".

in history.

The advent of the jet engine now began to impinge upon piston engine development. By 1944, virtually every country in the world involved in the development of aircraft had begun to understand the distinct advantages of the jet engine over the piston. Though fuel consumption rates remained high, metallurgical difficulties were not easily overcome, and airframes were still not fully capable of accommodating the jet engine's tremendous performance potential, there was little question among the more progressive members of the engineering community that turbojet propulsion was the wave of the future.

Consequent to the successful work being undertaken in the field of turbojet propulsion, peripheral elements also continued to explore the advantages of high-performance rocket propulsion systems. Carrying their own oxidizers and propellants, these staggeringly powerful engines could be used to move many tons over great ranges at extremely high rates of speed. Unfortunately, fuel consumption rates, questionable dependability, throttling difficulties, and safety prevented widespread use of the rocket in manned aircraft, but nevertheless, the Luftwaffe, during World War II undertook the development of several rocket-propelled point defense interceptors, including the notorious Messerschmitt Me 163.

Post-war development of the jet engine was rapid and expansive. Virtually every major country in the world with an aerospace industry embarked on programs calling for the development and utilization of jet powerplants in aircraft. U.S. efforts, which initially had centered on the country's lead in the related field of turbo-superchargers, had been boosted considerably by British asssistance in the form of technology and hardware transfers during the first few years of the war. This had resulted in the Bell XP-59 and the first U.S. jet flight on October 1, 1942, and later, in the rapid development of numerous post-war turbojet aircraft.

The Soviet Union, too, had benefitted from British generosity, as the consummation of an agreement formalizing the sale of a number of jet engines to the Soviet aircraft industry during the late 1940s eventually led to an indigenous jet engine industry of immense proportions. Soviet progress would not have been nearly so rapid without access to British technology, and aircraft such as the extraordinarily successful MiG-15 could not possibly have been developed.

Piston and jet engine development has continued at a steady pace throughout the history of aircraft technology. Today, as we approach the century mark following the first successful flight of the Wright Flyer, aircraft engines permitting non-stop flights around the world, speeds in excess of 20,000 mph, and altitudes that effectively encompass exo-atmospheric capabilities, are not only possible, but relatively commonplace. Much of this technology is personified by the displays in the Champlin Fighter Museum. From World War I rotary engines of less than 100 hp to state-of-the-art turbojet engines capable of producing in excess of 17,000 lbs. of thrust, virtually the entire spectrum of aircraft propulsion is covered in one form or another. A brief over-view of the engines on display in the museum follows:

Allison V-1710

The birth of the only mass-produced U.S. liquid-cooled engine to see service during World War II, and thus one of the most important piston engines of all time, can trace its origins back to the famous consortium-designed and consortium-produced Liberty engine of World War I. Allison, which entered the aviation arena during 1926 with an engine developed from the Liberty and referred to as the V-1410, slowly improved upon the basic design and by June of 1930, was offering the U.S. Navy a 650 hp twelve-cylinder dirigible powerplant designated V-1710-A. When completed and bench-tested during August of 1931, this engine proved quite impressive and relatively trouble-free. Importantly, it had the distinction of being the first aircraft engine of any kind designed from scratch to utilize ethylene glycol cooling.

Accidental destruction of the airship Macon led to cancellation of the V-1710 contract, but following sale of the Allison company to General Motors, the project was resurrected for further development. During 1937, flght testing of an early engine in the Curtiss XP-37 verified its great potential, and within a matter of months, a number of airframe manufacturers were ordering it in large quantities for use in their newest fighters. Included were Bell with their FM-1 and P-39; Curtiss with their P-40; Lockheed with their P-38; and North American with their P-51 (early versions only).

The V-1710's power increased steadily throughout the course of its production history. Early engines were good for 1,000 to 1,250 hp, whereas the later V-1710-143 was capable of developing over 2,300 hp. Allison went on to build over 47,000 V-1710s before production was terminated.

Clerget

In an attempt to eliminate some of the major failings of the original Gnome rotary engine design, Frenchman Pierre Clerget and his engineering staff during 1911 began development of a new rotary engine that was designed to offer significant improvements in fuel and lubricant consumption. In conquering these failings, the Gnome design was heavily modified so that the fuel/oil mix was transferred from the crankcase to the combustion chambers through external piping, rather than via valves in the pistons. Additionally, inlet and exhaust valves were mounted conventionally on the tops of each cylinder and actuated by pushrods.

The design proved quite successful, and though never to usurp the Le Rhone/Gnome competition, maintained a position of equality until the demise of the rotary engine's prominence as an aircraft powerplant. Thousands of Clerget rotarys eventually were built, with production being undertaken in Great Britain as well as France.

There were many different Clerget models manufactured. The initial production versions had seven-cylinders, later models had nine-cylinders, and still later models had eleven-cylinders. Horsepower ratings varied from 80 to 200.

General Electric J47

General Electric's early dominance in the field

Germany's WWII-vintage Junkers Jumo 213 was a large, liquid-cooled engine with a high power-to-weight ratio.

Gnome 100 hp rotary had one valve per cylinder.

of first-generation U.S. jet engines was directly attributable to the company's very early involvement in the development of high-temperature turbo-superchargers for piston engines. Under the aegis of a 1941 Army contract, work was begun on the TG-100 turboprop, and this culminated in successful application of the T31 engine to the Convair XP-81 fighter and a first flight during December of 1945. In the interim, the company was privileged to be chosen by Gen. H. Arnold to build a U.S. version of the British W.1 turbojet engine then being developed by Frank Whittle and his Power Jets, Ltd. The resulting engine, called the Type I, was run for the first time on April 18, 1942. Following improvements suggested by Whittle to overcome temperature anomalies, a revised version was developed and successfully utilized in the first U.S. jet aircraft, the Bell XP-59.

A number of interim jet engines followed, these eventually leading to the TG-180 which proved extraordinarily successful under its more commonly utilized name of J35. Contractual complications caused General Electric to turn over production of this engine to Allison, but in the meantime, a more advanced engine, initially referred to as the TG-190, was placed in development. Eventually known as the J47, the first full-up example was bench-tested for the first time on June 21, 1947 and by mid-1948, was in production.

With the outbreak of the Korean War, demand for the J47 increased exponentially due primarily to its use in the North American F-86—the only U.S. counter to the agile MiG-15. Coupled with

the rapid increase in Boeing B-47 production—which used no less than six J47s—by the end of 1954, nearly a thousand engines per month were being rolled from General Electric factories. By the time production ended in 1956, some 36,500 J47s had been completed.

The J47 was built in a large number of versions for a great variety of applications. Initial non-afterburning engines were generally rated at approximately 4,000 lbs. thrust, whereas the final production versions, fully-equipped with afterburners, generated 7,650 lbs. thrust.

General Electric J79

Unquestionably the most successful of all U.S. supersonic turbojet engines, General Electric's J79 was born as a design study during 1951 and came into being as an official company project during October of the following year. Incorporating the then-technologically-advanced system of variable-stator blades in its compressor section, the new engine was formally designated J79 by the Air Force in November and bench tested (compressor demonstrator only) for the first time during August of 1953. By June of the following year, the full engine was undergoing static testing and this was followed by airborne tests under a North American B-45 during May of 1955. First flight by an aircraft powered only by the J79 took place on December 8, 1955, when a modified Douglas F4D became airborne from Edwards AFB with the engine in place of its normal Pratt & Whitney J57.

Part of the justification for the J79 was its

applicability to a new bomber project then underway at Convair. Eventually to become known as the B-58, this aircraft became the world's first supersonic bomber and the holder of numerous world speed and altitude records. Later J79 applications included the Lockheed F-104 (the first U.S. jet aircraft capable of Mach 2 in level flight), the Grumman F11F-1F, and perhaps most importantly, both the Air Force and Navy versions of the ubiquitous F-4. Early J79s were rated at approximately 14,350 lbs. thrust in afterburner and later versions at 17,820 lbs. During the course of its production life, J79-powered aircraft set 46 world records. No less than 17,000 J79s were manufactured by General Electric and its licensees by the time production ended during the late 1970s.

Junkers-Jumo 213

A man of great engineering talent and considerable energy, Prof. Hugo Junkers began his professional aviation career during 1913 when he designed and built (as an aside to the marine engine work he was accommodating already) a small aircraft diesel called the MO-3. Steady development of this initial incursion into the aircraft propulsion system market resulted in ever-increasing orders for Junkers products, and coupled with a decision to design and build full-scale aircraft of all-metal construction (considered a major innovation during the latter years of World War I), the Junkers company grew rapidly even following Germany's collapse during 1918.

A lengthy series of successful diesel and con-

tion of a separate engine division known as Junkers Motorenbau (referred to as Jumo) and brought the company considerable success during the between-the-war years. Riding on the coattails of Hitler's ascent to power, Junkers aircraft engines and aircraft became a fixture of more than passing importance in the history of the rapidly expanding Luftwaffe.

During 1933, as just one facet of a sizable engine development program, Junkers unveiled its Jumo 210 and 211 inverted V-12s. Conventionally carburetted and cooled with glycol (Glysantin), they differed from each other primarily in displacement. The 210 eventually found its way into the Messerschmitt Bf 109C and the 211 into the Ju 87A. In both instances, they proved highly reliable and efficient.

The 211 later became the basis for the exceptionally advanced Jumo 213. Optimized for continuous operation at 3,000 rpm, it initially was rated at 1,776 hp while weighing only 2,028 lbs. The 213J version, equipped with 4 valves per cylinder, was rated at no less than 2,600 hp. Though large, the Jumo 213 was nevertheless utilized in several German combat aircraft, not the least of which was the Focke Wulf FW 190D and Tank Ta 152 series. Capable of speeds well in excess of 450 mph, these fighters were considered the ultimate Focke Wulf piston-engined aircraft of the war and probably also represented the ultimate German piston-engined fighters of all time.

Le Rhone 80HP

As mentioned earlier in the text, the first viable rotary engine was developed in France by Gnome during 1907. The success of this powerplant pushed the company into prominence in a very short period of time, and by 1914, it was able to buy out one of its main competitors, the Soc des Moteurs Le Rhone company which had initiated production of indigenously designed rotary engines during 1910. The resulting operation proved highly successful and evolved an extensive series of rotary engines that were designated according to horsepower—either 80, 110, 130, or 180, depending on the number of cylinders and their displacement. Variations on the theme were manufactured in Sweden, the U.S., the Soviet Union, Germany, and other countries. The engines were used with considerable success in a variety of World War I fighter and light bomber aircraft, and were in fact the dominant powerplant of the war until early 1917.

Pratt & Whitney R-2800

During 1936, in the middle of the tremendous success being enjoyed by the R-1830, Pratt & Whitney's engineering team moved ahead with plans to manufacture a significantly more powerful engine in the form of the R-2800 Double Wasp with eighteen-cylinders and over 2,000 hp. This engine, like its immediate predecessor, was an almost instantaneous success, and within a short period of time was being utilized in such notable fighters as the Air Force's Republic P-47 and the Navy's Vought F4U. In the latter aircraft, with a rating of some 2,000 hp, it became the first air-cooled radial engine in the world to power a production 400 mph fighter.

Because of the exigencies of war and the demand for powerplants, the R-2800, and numerous other Pratt & Whitney engines were co-manufactured by other companies. Both Chevrolet and Nash-Kelvinator eventually became involved in R-2800 production, with parts being supplied by a large number of sub-contractors.

Pratt & Whitney R4360

Pratt & Whitney's R-4360 was unquestionably the most powerful mass-produced aircraft piston engine ever manufactured in the U.S. With no less than 28 cylinders, 56 sparkplugs, and a whole host of other physical superlatives that remain almost too many to mention, it was indeed an awesome exercise in engineering and technology.

The R-4360 was actually the result of Pratt & Whitney's penchant for radial, air-cooled engines. Military requirements, and the Air Force's infatuation with liquid-cooled V-type engines had forced the company to explore different technologies, but its confidence in the attributes of the air-cooled radial eventually caused the War Department to rethink its own approach to its propulsion needs. Accordingly, when Pratt & Whitney was asked to build a liquid-cooled engine, it stood firm in its belief that the radial was more appropriate, and eventually convinced Gen. H. Arnold that a powerful air-cooled radial could be developed in considerably less time than a liquid-cooled V-type. Arnold agreed with the argument, and in short order, the R-4360 Wasp Major was born.

Though large, complex, and heavy, the R-4360 was utilized in one fighter (the Goodyear F2G) and a fairly large number of bombers and transports including the Convair B-36, the Boeing C-97, and the Boeing B-50. During 1942, when it debuted, it was rated at 3,000 hp; by the middle of 1945, it was producing over 3,500 hp. Many years later, racing-modified R-4360s were generating close to 4,500 hp at full throttle.

Walter HWK 509

During 1935, Prof. Hellmuth Walter, whose formal background was in research chemistry, founded Helmuth Walter Kommanditgesellschaft (HWK) and embarked on a program to develop small rocket engines for experimentation and air-

craft propulsion. During 1936 he completed work on a small booster for the Heinkel He 72, and in turn followed this with a series of rocket-assisted-takeoff units for a variety of other aircraft. Further work resulted in contracts for rocket engines to power the experimental Heinkel He 76 and DFS 194 (the former being the world's first liquid-fuel pure rocket aircraft), and this in turn was followed by a contract to develop an engine for the Messerschmitt Me 163 rocket-propelled interceptor.

In all cases, these engines utilized hypergolic propellants wherein the mixing of T-stoff (80% peroxide/stabilizer) and Z-stoff (strong calcium permanganate solution) would lead to spontaneous combustion. By the advent of the Me 163's definitive R-II-211—which later was designated HWK-509—Z-stoff had been replaced by the slightly less cantankerous C-stoff (30% solution of hydrazine hydrate in methanol). Regardless, the extremely volatile nature of these propellant combinations quickly gave the Walter engines a reputation for being both pilot and ground crew killers. More frequently than not, partially expended fuel loads exploded after the Me 163 had undertaken a mission, usually completely destroying the aircraft and taking the pilot with it.

The first-generation HWK-509A found in virtually all Me 163s was nominally rated at 3,748 lbs. thrust at altitude. The second-generation HWK-509C, equipped with a cruise chamber giving the aircraft considerably extended duration, was rated at 4,409 lbs. thrust at altitude and was found only in the Messerschmitt Me 263 and the Bachem Ba 349.

The Walter HWK 509 rocket engine was utilized to power the unconventional Messerschmitt Me 163.

Pratt & Whitney R-2800 powered many WWII fighters.

Junkers Jumo 213 powered the Fw 190D-13.

"Taube" was powered by a Mercedes six-cylinder engine.

Roy Grinnell's steller S.E. 5A painting is one of many such works on display in the Museum by this and other talented aviation artists.

AUTOMATIC WEAPONS COLLECTION

Collecting machine guns was, and still is, an area of unique specialization. For one, laws prohibiting the collection, use, and distribution of such weapons are extraordinarily restrictive, and for another, few individuals have the time, money, or inclination to accommodate the bureaucratic roadblocks that almost always stand in the way of acquisitions. Making such collecting even more challenging is the fact that the uniqueness of a weapon is dependent on a great number of somewhat ill-defined variables, not the least of which are rarity and previous ownership. In some cases, and unlike most aircraft, production of a machine gun variant or sub-variant remains virtually undocumented, and thus little if any information remains to provide an owner with insight into the weapon's value or significance.

As noted in his short autobiographical sketch, Doug, during 1987, acquired from fellow collector J. Curtis Earl what many authorities consider to be the world's finest privately-owned machine gun collection. As displayed, it is named after Earl and consumes over 3,000 sq. ft. of floor space in a special vault built between the two aircraft hangars. Many of the weapons in this superb collection can be seen no where else in the world--as they represent the only extant examples known.

Earl's collection is the result of more than fifty years' work. His first acquisitions were made as early as 1933 when relatives and family friends (including Utah's then-Secretary of State

Welling) gave him hardware (including two rare Maxims) they had acquired during World War I.

After graduating Bear River High School, Earl attended Utah State and majored in wildlife management. Peripheral interests also were exercised, with significant expertise being developed in engineering, physics, chemistry, and photography. He later worked for the Utah Fish and Game Commission, the U.S. Fish and Wildlife Service, the Missouri Conservation Commission, and finally, the Arizona Game and Fish Department. In between, he acquired experience in quality control, real estate sales, commercial contracting, and gold mining, and even managed to take time off to acquire his pilot's license on the side. By 1965, Earl was one of only three privately-licensed machine gun dealers in the U.S. Conveniently, he was the only dealer in the West (as this is written, there now are about 10,000 Class III--post-1968 classification--U.S. machine gun dealers).

"I obtained my first machine guns at age nine. They were two MG 08/15s from an American Legion post in Utah, which was disposing of its WWI memorabilia since the Boy Scouts were cutting up one another with bayonets and whatnot. My father was asked to dump all the material in a river, but I asked if I could keep the MGs. He said I could, provided I transported them home, which I did with my bicycle.

"Subsequent additions were an MP-40 as a birthday present from my wife, and a Thompson M-3 *Grease Gun* from the Chandler, Arizona

Chief of Police. After that the assembly grew 'normally' for a collector.

"Just as museum aircraft are divided into originals, reproductions and replicas, I consider the weapons collection to be broadly categorized as 'personality pieces', rarities and unique specimens. Several of the guns displayed at the Champlin Fighter Museum are linked to local or world figures, and in some ways these pieces are the most fascinating of all.

"Maj. Russell Burnam represents a personality who was active in Arizona, Mexico and points east. His Maxim M-89 (serial no. 637) dates from his days as Chief of Scouts for the British during the Boar War. However, the remarkable adventurer began his career as a teenager in the American Southwest, where he walked a none-too-cautious line between the law and outlaws. In his autobiography he admits that he skipped Arizona following the Pleasant Valley War, one or two jumps ahead of the law. While in Mexico he was drawn to Africa by Cecil Rhodes, founder of Rhodesia long before that independent nation became Zimbabwe.

"The Mexican border also was the venue of two other guns on display: a Lewis Gun (14327) purchased by nortorious bandito Pancho Villa, and the Arizona Rangers' M1895 Marlin (12340). Villa ordered four Lewises but all were intercepted by U.S. authorities before he took delivery. The Marlin, one of two the Rangers owned, is further distinguished by matching serial numbers on all accessories and equipment.

"Among the aviation weapons on display, perhaps the star item is the M1914 Lewis made by St. Etienne Arsenal in France. It was taken from the Hanriot HD-1 that French ace Charles Nungesser flew in this country after WWI, and was acquired by Col. G.B. Jarrett. Years later Frank Tallman of the famed Tallmantz Museum in California obtained the gun, and I bought it from Frank.

"At the end of World War II a U.S. Army team was present when Soviet troops entered Adlof Hitler's bunker. The American colonel brought back a mint-condition MP-41 (26570), which is one of only five of the type known in the United States. Naturally, many other guns and artifacts were 'liberated' from the Fuhrer's Bunker but probably no accounting ever was made by any Allied power.

"The end of the World War II also spawned the M-1A1 Thompson (85004), one of four presentation pieces prepared by Savage Arms. They were to have gone to the President, Generals Eisenhower and MacArthur, and Admiral Nimitz. However, for unknown reasons the weapons never were presented and the oval plates on the stocks were not engraved.

"Another World War II 'personality' weapon also is featured in the collection: a Japanese Type 92 machine gun (27536) captured by the First Marine Division on Guadalcanal in November 1942. The division commander, Brig. Gen. Archer Vandergrift, gave it to Vice Admiral W.F. Halsey, Commander Southwest Pacific Forces. Rear Admiral Nickol of Halsey's staff

A sampling of the Museum's machine gun collection.

The Museum's Thompson sub-machine gun collection is considered to be one of the world's finest.

Glass enclosures house machine gun samples.

was given the gun and Earl obtained the gun from him.

"Two Vietnam War trophies are on display, one ironically from a fighter pilot, Lt. Col. Jim Empey, a World War II ace who served in Vietnam at the same time as his son. He brought back an AK-47 (11078529) which I obtained from him. Similarly, Sgt. Barry Sadler--author of the hit song 'Ballad of the Green Berets'--captured a Viet Cong Mk I Bren Gun (V 299).

"Among the items I classify as rarities are some sets of weapons rather than a single piece. The Browning Automatic Rifle (BAR) collection includes all four U.S. production models, including the Colt Monitor variant (100206), of which only some 50 were produced for law enforcement.

"Twenty-odd Thompsons are displayed at the Champlin Fight Museum, including the original Model 1921-28 Navy contract gun (10398), with Enfield compensator.

"The Italian Villar Perosa (S1637, D1637) has been called the first sub-machine gun. However, its dual-mount configuration that produced 3,000-rounds per minute was more adaptable to aircraft use. Designed in 1915, it was only used in limited quantities late in World War I. This is one of only three known in the United States.

"Though hundreds of thousands of Soviet PPSh 41s were made, the blond wood and

chrome-nickel plating on No. 354 makes it rare indeed. When the Soviet Consul from San Francisco decided to sample the fleshy pleasures of Las Vegas, he attempted to enter a casino with his body guard in tow. The security folks, being touchy about such things, convinced their Russian guests that the sub-machine gun should remain in 'protective custody' of the police. But the Soviets neglected to pick up the PPSh when they left town and eventually I acquired the piece at auction.

"Two more aviation pieces represent examples of armament from the fabulous Japanese Zero fighter of World War II. These are a Type 41 (486) copy of the Browning M-2 in 12.7mm and the Type 89 (1065ECC) Vickers duplicate in 7.7mm. Several other Japanese weapons are displayed as well.

"Another Arizona connection is the M1910 Benet-Mercier machine gun (serial 505). It was used by the Army in defense of Columbus, New Mexico against Villa's forces, but the U.S. troops found they could not operate it at night. The stripper-clip feed system gave no feel of up or down, left or right.

"Occasionally mounts are rarer and therefore more valuable than the guns they support. Cases in point are the superbly-engineered mounts for German's MG-34 and MG-42 of World War II. The museum's examples show

how the lightweight, highly portable tripods can be adjusted to cover almost any desired field of fire--nothing remotely comparable is made today.

"The unique specimens category is the largest of the collection, and it is only possible to hit the high points. But surely the German items rate among the most intriguing. The Mk 108 aircraft cannon (24939) is the only one registered to a civilian in the U.S., representative of main armament from nearly every Luftwaffe fighter of World War II. Similarly, the MG-81 (40027/38) twin-barrel aircraft weapon is remarkable. The aircrewman's hand-held mount spat out 3,000-rounds of 8mm per minute, and was adaptable to ground use if forced down in hostile territory.

"Among infantry weapons, the Bergmann MP-18 (18052) was the first true sub-machine gun. Its military use was limited but it found wide acceptance among police units with 20- and 32-round magazines. The prototype MP-38 (2065a), widely misnamed 'Schmeisser', was the forerunner of what we recognize today as true military sub-machine guns.

"Small arms development peaked in World War II, and you won't get much argument by claiming that one of the most influential types was the excellent FG-42. Only some 7,000 were made, exclusively for paratroop use, and the Champlin Fighter Museum's (7392) is one of just 11 in the U.S. Even more rare is the MP-44 Krummlauf variant, with curved barrel and prism sight for shooting around corners; only two others are known in this country.

"Unique Thompsons are not hard to catalog but they are extremely difficult to acquire. The world's only complete 'Tommy Gun' collection is defined by the 9mm (S1), the only such weapon in civilian hands anywhere. Only slightly harder to find is the M1927 semi-automatic model (5252). Some 42 were registered, and of 17 still known I have owned eleven.

"But the *creme de la creme* is the 'Midas Thompson' by Colt's master engraver, Earl C. Bieu. The elaborate scrollwork, including that on the magazine, is exceptional, but the 24-karat inlayed wire and burlwalnut stocks enhance an overall effect that truly is more than the sum of its parts. No finer example of the gunsmith's art exists anywhere.

"Wartime products to augment the Thompson included the Reising M-55. The Champlin Fighter Museum weapon (65492) is one of two known original Marine Corps Reisings remaining in this country.

"Consecutive serial numbers always are of special interest to collectors, but matched sets of machine guns are even harder to find. The M1919s (C100257/58) on Colt tripods are two of only three known in the world.

"Not quite as rare, but still noteworthy, is the

Japanese Type 100 SMG (2726). All three Japanese training machine guns on dispaly were capable of firing reduced-load ammunition in emergencies.

"Aside from automatic weapons, five light to medium cannon are slated for display at the Champlin Fighter Museum. They range from 25- to 75mm, representing five different countries. They include the U.S. 'pack howitzer' of World War II, plus 25mm antitank guns from Finland and France plus 37mm Swedish Bofors and German Pak types.

"Finally, in the 'nongun' category is the wagon-wheel antiaircraft mount for World War I machine guns. The museum display uses a Lewis, but in the motion pictures *Dawn Patrol* and *Lilac Time* this very mount used a Maxim to defend the generic German aerodrome from Allied attack.

"In summarizing the collection, I should emphasize that it consists of many sub-collections. Whether by nationality or by type, this assembly of automatic weapons represents a lifetime of scrounging, work--and fun."

J. Curtis Earl

Machine guns occupy an odd legal status, and so civilians are less likely to be familiar with them and their operating principles and terminology than with aircraft. Though civilian-owned machine guns are tightly regulated, they are legal. This Earl collection includes more types, variants, and subvariants than virtually any other collection open to the general public.

The following is a glossary of the collection's weapon categories and operating systems:

TYPES

Sub-machine Gun–an individual weapon of rifle weight or lighter, firing a pistol cartridge or pistol-type cartridge. Physically much smaller than a rifle of similar vintage, but substantially larger than a service pistol.

Machine Pistol–a pistol or pistol-sized weapon capable of fully automatic fire. May employ a detachable or folding stock for shoulder use, but is capable of convenient operation in some fashion with one hand.

Automatic Rifle–usually a selective-fire, rifle-configuration weapon, substantially heavier than a standard infantry rifle but otherwise similar in layout, sights, etc. Often employs a bipod, virtually always employs an easily-detached box magazine of forty rounds or less capacity. An individual weapon, but often employing team tactics wherein a loader ammunition carrier acts in support of the weapon's operator/gunner.

Assault Rifle–a standard infantry rifle designed for or adapted to selective fire, often in the "medium" loading between full-power rifle ammunition and pistol calibers, as with the U.S. .223/5.56mm and Soviet 7.62x39mm rounds.

Light Machine Gun–a standard, small-unit support weapon with limited sustained fire characteristics, usually somewhat heavier than an automatic rifle. Almost always has a quick-change barrel. May feed from belt or box magazine, or sometimes interchange as necessary. Always employs some sort of integral bipod.

General Purpose Machine Gun–a machine gun approximating the light machine gun in basic shape and size, but which generally has a heavier or longer barrel, and which can be used from more liberal sustained, fix-position fire. Virtually always capable of belt feed, though magazines may be employed for special applications, and always capable of adaptation to tripod mounting. Always at least nominally crew-served, since these weapons play very important tactical roles and it is always presumed they will consume considerable ammunition.

Medium Machine Gun–primary crew-served support infantry weapon, usually intended solely for operation from tripods or other stable mounts. Virtually always belt-fed. Usually, in its operating mode, a medium machine gun cannot be carried over distance by a single man. While "medium" generally refers to the gun's weight and bulk, medium machine gun receivers generally are very sturdy and heavy duty, and have evolved in such a manner that they no longer even resemble rifles.

Heavy Machine Gun–a crew-served weapon, often of a caliber heavier than standard infantry rifles, intended for relatively long, sustained bursts without compromising the barrel or breech parts. Usually heavy machine guns are capable of accurate bursts to 1,000 meters or more. Most water-cooled machine guns are considered heavies. Always used on a tripod or other fixed mount. Incapable of transport over distance by a single, fully-equipped infantryman, and generally travels as components.

None of these subdivisions is ironclad, especially since the introduction in the 1950s of assault rifle cartridges. Even some sub-machine guns were adapted to mounts, and some countries have modified designs for extremely unusual applications, but the roles in which guns serve generally fit these categories, even if the hardware does not. Aircraft guns, of course, are all "wild card", tucked in where possible and as necessary to deliver a maximum of firepower, and fit only very loosely into any of these categories.

OPERATING SYSTEMS

All semi-automatic and automatic systems begin with an explosion inside the cartridge. Sealed behind the bullet, expanding gasses impart forward movement to the bullet, rearward movement to the cartridge case and whatever is behind it. Pressure from cartridge ignition may range as high as 60,000 pounds per square inch or higher. In conventional firearms, this energy merely converts to recoil, gross movement of the entire weapon back toward the firer.

Semi-automatic and automatic weapons use the energy to extract and eject the cartridge case just fired, and to chamber a fresh cartridge. Semi-automatics or selective fire automatics interrupt or sear off ignition of the subsequent shots by mechanically inhibiting the hammer or striker from activating the firing pin. Automatics cycle and fire until the ammunition is exhausted or the trigger released.

Gas operation in an automatic weapon involves ducting the barrel somewhere aft of the muzzle and using the gasses behind the bullet to push an operating rod, piston, or sometimes, the bolt itself to the rear.

Recoil systems lock barrel and breech together, fully or partway to the rear, using the aft thrust of the cartridge casing to impart the recoiling effect.

In blowback guns, the same cartridge thrust is used to impart rearward movement, but only the bolt/breech mechanism actually moves.

In all cases, return or recoil springs turn this action around to chamber the fresh round and reinitiate the cycle. Providing delay or locking– the time gap necessary to assure that high pressure no longer exists at the breech when the cartridge is ejected--may be performed by camming, sprung bearings, positive lock to other components, weight, or combinations of spring tension and mass.

Many guns combine two or more operating systems. And there are a few other, obscure operating systems.

Most weapons in automatic operation fire from the open bolt, wherein the breech remains open when not actually firing. This is intended to dissipate heat and prevent cook-offs, wherein a hot chamber begins igniting rounds without interacting with firing pin or trigger. This is less important with short-magazined guns and many aircraft applications (these two categories constitute most of the exceptions to the rule).

Cooling systems today amount to heavy barrels and air cooling, which is really cooling by mass and patience. Liquid cooling was very effective, and was used to great advantage in both

MiG-15 had two 23mm m.g. and one 37mm cannon.

world wars, but added weight to guns (for the water itself and the jackets), and so has passed out of use.

Heat builds up very rapidly in machine guns. Heat and ammunition supply are the reasons why actual delivered fire rates are much slower than measured rates of fire. For example, a Thompson sub-machine gun will dispose of ammunition for the duration of a burst at the rate of 550-850 rounds per minute. But the largest magazine is 100 rounds, and therefore, actual practical rate of bullet delivery is far lower. Some aircraft wing or cowl guns can deliver all their ammunition at the rate of 1,500 rounds per minute per gun, but the ammunition supply is seldom more than 300 rounds per gun. Inflight reloading is impossible.

One further note: Machine guns are dependent on ammunition pressure/velocity for their operation. Erratic ammunition can cause malfunctions with the very best of these weapons, and some of those malfunctions can be dangerous, even deadly.

NAME: Maxim
MODEL: 1889
CALIBER: 7.92mm
COUNTRY: Germany
MANUFACTURER: Maxim
CYCLIC RATE OF FIRE: 300 rpm*
SYSTEM OF OPERATION(S): recoil
TYPE OF FIRE: full auto
AMMUNITION DELIVERY BY: cloth belt
SERIAL NO.: 637

COMMENTS: This 1889 Maxim was the personal machine gun of Maj. Burnam, a soldier of fortune who rented his services and weapon. Most of his fame came from commanding a scouting unit in South Africa against a native uprising in the late 19th century.

NAME: Schwarzlose
MODEL: Modell 07/12
CALIBER: 8mm
COUNTRY: Austria
MANUFACTURER: Osterreichische Waffenfabrik, Steyr
CYCLIC RATE OF FIRE: 400 rpm*
SYSTEM OF OPERATION(S): blowback
TYPE OF FIRE: full auto
AMMUNITION DELIVERY BY: internal magazine
SERIAL NO.: 39694

COMMENTS: The foremost machine gun for the Austrian's in WWI, the Schwarzlose was a simple and strong design, but suffered in combat from stoppages due to adverse conditions and ammunition irregularities. It was also adapted to aircraft with little success.

* = rounds per minute

NAME: Madsen
MODEL: 1904
CALIBER: 7.92mm
COUNTRY: Denmark
MANUFACTURER: Madsen or Disa
CYCLIC RATE OF FIRE: 450 rpm
SYSTEM OF OPERATION(S): recoil
TYPE OF FIRE: full auto
AMMUNITION DELIVERY BY: 25-, 30- or 40-round box magazine
SERIAL NO.: 0094

COMMENTS: Undoubtedly the Madsen was one of the first and finest light machine guns ever produced. Essentially the same gun was produced for over 50 yrs. and was sold to over 34 countries, although never adopted by any major country. Remarkable for its innovations and ingenious design it was a considerable commercial success and was copied widely.

NAME: Lewis
MODEL: 1914
CALIBER: .303
COUNTRY: Great Britain
MANUFACTURER: BSA
CYCLIC RATE OF FIRE: 550 rpm
SYSTEM OF OPERATION(S): gas
TYPE OF FIRE: full auto
AMMUNITION DELIVERY BY: 47- or 97-round pan magazine
SERIAL NO.: A127

COMMENTS: The Lewis light machine gun was the first light automatic, to be used on a large scale in time of war. It was mass produced and adopted by the U.S. Army in the last of WWI, although the designer, Col. Isaac Lewis, was an American. Its principal virtue was that it was the first in the field: its drawbacks were excessive weight and stoppages due to its complicated mechanism.

NAME: Lewis Light Machine Gun
MODEL: 1914 MK III
CALIBER: .303
COUNTRY: Great Britain
MANUFACTURER: BSA
CYCLIC RATE OF FIRE: 450-500 rpm
SYSTEM OF OPERATION(S): full auto only
TYPE OF FIRE:
AMMUNITION DELIVERY BY: 47- or 97-round magazine
SERIAL NO.: A1237

COMMENTS: The Lewis Gun not only played a major role in aerial warfare in WWI, but it was extensively used by the individual combat infantryman for a multi-purpose weapon including air defense. In fact, British historians credit the Lewis with shooting down more low-flying enemy aircraft than any other gun in their inventory. In this diarama the gun is mounted on a wagon wheel at an American aerodrome in WWI, with an American flying officer watching the combat of Lt. Douglas Campbell scoring the first American Air Service victory over a German Albatros. The binoculars are German. This gun and wagon wheel were bought from the Tallmantz movie collection and starred in many WWI films including *Dawn Patrol* with Errol Flynn and David Niven. The uniform was worn by Lt. Maurice Kevin Dwyer in WWI, although he was not present at the depicted combat. The cap and English flying suit belonged to American ace, Joe Wehner, killed in combat defending his wingman and friend, Frank Luke. The cross is from a German bomber. The roundel is from American ace Hamilton Coolidge's Nieuport 27.

NAME: Vickers Aircraft Machine Gun
MODEL: Mark 1
CALIBER: 11mm
COUNTRY: Britain
MANUFACTURER: various United Kingdom arsenals
CYCLIC RATE OF FIRE: 550 rpm
SYSTEM OF OPERATION(S): recoil
TYPE OF FIRE: full auto only
AMMUNITION DELIVERY BY: fabric web belt
SERIAL NO.: 945, A1646, A2001

COMMENTS: This Vickers gun is fitted with its top-mounted engine synchronizer bar to prevent shots striking the propeller of the aircraft. It is also equipped with a small flash suppressor scoop under the muzzle. This is the type most commonly found mounted on S.P.A.D.s and *Camel* fighter aircraft. These guns were equipped with a remote firing cable with a trigger affixed to the pilot's joy stick. The Vickers was commonly used in single or dual mounts. This gun is 11mm caliber, which was designed as a "balloon buster" cartridge. The 11mm was large enough to insert a small amount of gun powder in the base of the bullet, so the bullet tended to ignite the hydrogen-filled balloons, bringing them down in flames. It was also found to be far more effective in air-to-air combat than the .303 cartridge. After WWI Vickers continued to be used by all of the allied countries but were subsequently phased out in preference to lighter and faster-firing guns.

NAME: Chauchat
MODEL: 1915
CALIBER: 8mm
COUNTRY: France
MANUFACTURER: unknown
CYCLIC RATE OF FIRE: 250 rpm
SYSTEM OF OPERATION(S): gas
TYPE OF FIRE: full auto
AMMUNITION DELIVERY BY: 20-round box magazine
SERIAL NO.: CSBC 78391

COMMENTS: Having the distinction of being the worst-designed machine gun of WWI, the French compounded the error by utilizing inferior materials in the gun. The result was disaster and the gun was literally out of action most of its career.

NAME: Hotchkiss
MODEL: 1914
CALIBER: 8mm
COUNTRY: France
MANUFACTURER: Hotchkiss & CIE
CYCLIC RATE OF FIRE: 600 rpm
SYSTEM OF OPERATION(S): gas
TYPE OF FIRE: full auto
AMMUNITION DELIVERY BY: metallic strip belt
SERIAL NO.: 231139

COMMENTS: Adopted by the French army in 1897, the Hotchkiss was one of the first machine guns to be gas operated. It was heavy, but fairly reliable although the strip feed system caused problems. The Japanese copied and refined the Hotchkiss to become their primary heavy machine gun in WWII.

NAME: Hotchkiss
MODEL: 1914
CALIBER: 8mm
COUNTRY: France
MANUFACTURER: Hotchkiss at CIE
CYCLIC RATE OF FIRE: 600 rpm
SYSTEM OF OPERATION(S): gas
TYPE OF FIRE: full auto
AMMUNITION DELIVERY BY: 24- or 30-round metallic strips
SERIAL NO.: 231139

COMMENTS: Hotchkiss bought the design in 1893 from an Austrian inventor when only Browning and Maxim had working machine gun patents. An American, Laurence Benet, redesigned and perfected the design for Hotchkiss and the gun proved itself admirably during WWI. It was sold to many countries following the war.

NAME: Lewis Aircraft Light Machine Gun
MODEL: 1914
CALIBER: .303 British
COUNTRY: France
MANUFACTURER: St. Etienne
CYCLIC RATE OF FIRE: n/a
SYSTEM OF OPERATION(S): gas
TYPE OF FIRE: full auto only
AMMUNITION DELIVERY BY: 97-round drum magazine
SERIAL NO.: 3139

COMMENTS: This particular gun was owned by Charles Nungesser, France's third-leading ace in WWI with 45 victories. Nungesser brought this gun along with his Hanriot fighter plane to the U.S. shortly after the war to tour the country. Later he was killed with his fellow pilot when they attempted an Atlantic crossing shortly before Charles A. Lindbergh made his successful flight. Later Nungesser's aircraft with the mounted Lewis ended up in the possession of Col. G.B. Jarrett's aircraft collection. The Hanriot was subsequently transferred to the Paul Mantz aircraft collection in Orange County, California where it was used in WWI aircraft movies. Sometime later the aircraft and the gun parted company. The Lewis stayed in the Tallmantz Collection and was later purchased directly from Frank Tallman. The gun has been in the Curtis Earl Collection since that time. This St. Etienne-manufactured Lewis is the only French model known in the U.S. or the United Kingdom.

NAME: Hotchkiss Aircraft Machine Gun
MODEL: MK-1
CALIBER: .303 British
COUNTRY: Britain
MANUFACTURER: Enfield, England
CYCLIC RATE OF FIRE: 550 rpm
SYSTEM OF OPERATION(S): gas
TYPE OF FIRE: selective
AMMUNITION DELIVERY BY: tempered metal strip holding 9-, 14-, or 30-rounds
SERIAL NO.: A31679

COMMENTS: The Hotchkiss was the first machine gun employed by a fighter aircraft to fire through the propeller arc, greatly enhancing accuracy. A French pilot, Roland Garros, mounted the gun on his Morane-Saulnier in 1915 by using steel plates on his propeller to deflect the occasional bullet which hit the prop. However, the German Air Service soon adapted the Schneider patent for an interrupter gear (the first application of synchronizing a machine gun) to the Fokker Eindecker.

NAME: Spandau Light Machine Gun
MODEL: 1908-15
CALIBER: 7.92mm
COUNTRY: Germany
MANUFACTURER: Spandau Arsenal
CYCLIC RATE OF FIRE: 550 rpm
SYSTEM OF OPERATION(S): recoil
TYPE OF FIRE: full auto only
AMMUNITION DELIVERY BY: fabric web belt
SERIAL NO.: 392

COMMENTS: This version was employed as a swivel gun in balloons and zeppelins.

NAME: Spandau Light Machine Gun
MODEL: 1908-15
CALIBER: 7.92mm
COUNTRY: Germany
MANUFACTURER: Spandau Arsenal
CYCLIC RATE OF FIRE: 550 rpm
SYSTEM OF OPERATION(S): recoil
TYPE OF FIRE: full auto only
AMMUNITION DELIVERY BY: fabric web belt
SERIAL NO.: 6258

COMMENTS: This modification of the standard 08-15 German infantry weapon, modified and lightened for aircraft use, was their primary offensive and defensive weapon in WWI. Its design and versatility easily rates it as one of the world's finest machine guns. The Maxim was designed by an American engineer named Hiram Maxim. Mr. Maxim, finding little response to sales efforts in this country, presented it to Kaiser Wilhelm who immediately purchased manufacturing rights of the gun and put it into production for the German military. It was first manufactured as the Model 08 heavy machine gun. In 1915 the lightweight 08-15 was produced and later the aircraft machine gun as you see here, commonly known as the "Spandau", manufactured in the Spandau Arsenal. The little box at the rear of the receiver is the cartridge counter so that the pilot could tell at a glance how many cartridges remained.

COMMENTS: Two Spandaus mounted in Fokker D.VIII.

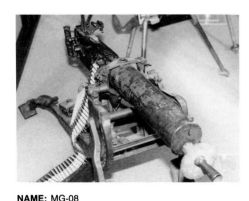

NAME: MG-08
MODEL: 1908
CALIBER: 7.92mm
COUNTRY: Germany
MANUFACTURER: Deutsche, Waffen & Munitions-fabriken, AG, Berlin
CYCLIC RATE OF FIRE: 450 rpm
SYSTEM OF OPERATION(S): recoil
TYPE OF FIRE: full auto
AMMUNITION DELIVERY BY: cloth belt
SERIAL NO.: 18791

COMMENTS: The American designer Hiram Maxim demonstrated his machine gun in Germany in 1887, and by 1908 the German Army was the first to be equipped with the Maxim design, the MG-08. The primary heavy machine gun for the Germans in WWI, it also served well into the 1930s until replaced by the MG-34. Shown here is its sled mount.

NAME: Dreyse
MODEL: 10
CALIBER: 7.92mm
COUNTRY: Germany
MANUFACTURER: R M & M
CYCLIC RATE OF FIRE: 700 rpm
SYSTEM OF OPERATION(S): blowback
TYPE OF FIRE: full auto
AMMUNITION DELIVERY BY: cloth belt
SERIAL NO.: 2206

COMMENTS: Although vastly overshadowed by the MG-08, the Dreyse was utilized in some numbers by WWI German units.

NAME: MG-08 (early version)
MODEL: 1908
CALIBER: 7.92mm
COUNTRY: Germany
MANUFACTURER: D W & M
CYCLIC RATE OF FIRE: 450 rpm
SYSTEM OF OPERATION(S): recoil
TYPE OF FIRE: full auto
AMMUNITION DELIVERY BY: cloth belt
SERIAL NO.: 3055

COMMENTS: This specimen is an early example of the MG-08.

NAME: MG-08/15
MODEL: 1908/15
CALIBER: 7.92mm
COUNTRY: Germany
MANUFACTURER: R M & M
CYCLIC RATE OF FIRE: 450 rpm
SYSTEM OF OPERATION(S): recoil
TYPE OF FIRE: full auto
AMMUNITION DELIVERY BY: cloth belt
SERIAL NO.: 8758B

COMMENTS: Since the MG-08 system weighed 137 lbs., the Germans issued a lighter version called the MG 08/15. This is a prime specimen with shoulder stock and bipod.

NAME: MP-18/1
MODEL: 18/1
CALIBER: 9mm
COUNTRY: Germany
MANUFACTURER: Bergmann
CYCLIC RATE OF FIRE: 400 rpm
SYSTEM OF OPERATION(S): blowback
TYPE OF FIRE: full auto
AMMUNITION DELIVERY BY: snail drum of 32-rounds
SERIAL NO.: 18052

COMMENTS: A landmark in the development of the true sub-machine gun, the MP-18/1 was designed by Hugo Schmeisser in 1916. Although the Beretta of 1918 was a close second, the MP-18/1 was the first true blowback design and set the pattern for sub-machine guns until 1938. It was relatively simple to manufacture as well as strong and reliable.

NAME: Villar Perosa
MODEL: 1915
CALIBER: 9mm
COUNTRY: Italy
MANUFACTURER: Fiat Spa, Canadian General Electric Co., Ltd.
CYCLIC RATE OF FIRE: 2400 rpm
SYSTEM OF OPERATION(S): delayed blowback
TYPE OF FIRE: full auto
AMMUNITION DELIVERY BY: 25-round box magazine
SERIAL NO.: S1637 & D1637

COMMENTS: Designed by an Italian officer, Abiel Bethel Revelli in 1915, it is considered to be the first sub-machine gun although the Italian Army didn't employ it in its proper role until the end of WWI. The gun was first used on aircraft and then as a light machine gun, but both uses proved unsuccessful with the light pistol cartridge.

NAME: Revelli
MODEL: 1914
CALIBER: 6.5mm
COUNTRY: Italy
MANUFACTURER: Fiat Spa
CYCLIC RATE OF FIRE: 400 rpm
SYSTEM OF OPERATION(S): delayed blowback
TYPE OF FIRE: full auto
AMMUNITION DELIVERY BY: 50-round strip-feed box
SERIAL NO.: 43172

COMMENTS: The 1914 Revelli was the first Italian designed machine gun to be produced in any numbers. The gun was unreliable due to its highly complicated feed mechanism and, with the low-powered 6.5mm rifle cartridge, it was no match for the Maxim or Browning designs.

NAME: Colt Light Machine Gun
MODEL: 1895
CALIBER: .30-1906
COUNTRY: U.S.A.
MANUFACTURER: Colt Firearms Co.
CYCLIC RATE OF FIRE: 450 rpm
SYSTEM OF OPERATION(S): gas
TYPE OF FIRE: full auto only
AMMUNITION DELIVERY BY: fabric web belt, 250-round capacity
SERIAL NO.: 103

COMMENTS: This particular gun is one of the earliest of its model known to exist. It is another brain child of the genius John M. Browning. This and many others were produced by the Colt Firearms Mfg. Co. under license by Browning. This machine gun was the first to employ the expanding gases of the cartridge channeled through a cylinder and operating against the operating bolt to maintain continuous fire. It was also unusual in that the gas was delivered through a small hole drilled into the barrel at the bottom, pushing against a camming piston which swung through an ark, operating the operating rod to make the fire continuous. This operating swing through an ark gave the impression of the old-style "potato digger", which was the nickname that was hung on the gun. It was also said that in a low mounted situation the operating rod dug a trench in the dirt and kicked it in the gunner's face, which also may have brought the nickname into usage. This was the machine gun the Americans used on San Juan Hil when Teddy Roosevelt's Rough Riders made their famous charge. It was also the primary American machine gun during the Philippine Insurrection and many other world-wide police actions that followed. The "potato digger" was widely marketed throughout the world.

NAME: Marlin Light Machine Gun
MODEL: Browning 1895
CALIBER: 7.62mm
COUNTRY: U.S.A.
MANUFACTURER: Marlin Firearms Mfg. Co.
CYCLIC RATE OF FIRE: 450 rpm
SYSTEM OF OPERATION(S): gas
TYPE OF FIRE: full auto only
AMMUNITION DELIVERY BY: fabric web belt
SERIAL NO.: 12340

COMMENTS: This Browning Model 1895, manufactured by Marlin Firearms Co., was originally owned by the Arizona Ranger Battalion. The Arizona Rangers owned two of these guns. Each was equipped with three extra barrels and a leather gun case for packing on their horses. In this set the gun, the tripod and all three extra barrels are marked with identical serial numbers.

NAME: Vickers Maxim Heavy Machine Gun
MODEL: 1904
CALIBER: .30-1906
COUNTRY: England
MANUFACTURER: Vickers, Sons, and Maxim Ltd.
CYCLIC RATE OF FIRE: 450 rpm
SYSTEM OF OPERATION(S): recoil
TYPE OF FIRE: full auto only
AMMUNITION DELIVERY BY: fabric web belt
SERIAL NO.: 75

COMMENTS: The U.S. Army bought nearly 300 1904 Vicker/Maxims in 1906. Seventy-seven guns were made in England by Vickers. The balance were subcontracted to Colt. This specimen was assigned to Ft. Riley, Kansas. It is only one of three existing in U.S. collections today.

NAME: Colt Vickers Medium Machine Gun
MODEL: Vickers 1918
CALIBER: .30-1906
COUNTRY: U.S.A.
MANUFACTURER: Colt Fire Arms Co.
CYCLIC RATE OF FIRE: 500 rpm
SYSTEM OF OPERATION(S): recoil
TYPE OF FIRE: full auto only
AMMUNITION DELIVERY BY: fabric web belt of 250-300 rounds
SERIAL NO.: 6404

COMMENTS: The Vickers gun, a modification of the Maxim design, was introduced in 1912 and remained in service with the British Army until 1968. It served with distinction with Lawrence in Arabia, Montgomery in North Africa, and Lord Mountbatten in Burma. This speciman was acquired by Earl from the MGM collection and has appeared in many films with Clark Gable, Humphrey Bogart, Edward G. Robinson, Wallace Beery and John Wayne.

NAME: Benet-Mercie Machine Rifle
MODEL: 1910
CALIBER: .30-1906
COUNTRY: France
MANUFACTURER: Colt U.S.A.
CYCLIC RATE OF FIRE: 450-500 rpm
SYSTEM OF OPERATION(S): gas
TYPE OF FIRE: selective
AMMUNITION DELIVERY BY: 30-round flat stripper clip feeding from the side
SERIAL NO.: 505

COMMENTS: This is one of only 670 Benet-Mercie Machine Rifles manufactured by the Colt and Springfield Armory for the U.S. Armed Services. Its small claim to fame was in 1916 when Pancho Villa raided Columbus, New Mexico and the U.S. Army defended the town with a Benet-Mercie. However, it is believed that not one of the guns used in that defense fired a single shot due to malfunctions. Pancho Villa's raid was at night and the U.S. troops couldn't load the guns because they couldn't see to put the stripper clip into the receivers. Henceforth, the guns were known as a daylight gun. The Mexican raiders used Colt, Browning, and Lewis guns during this battle, all of which worked very well.

NAME: Lewis Light Machine Gun
MODEL: 1917
CALIBER: .303 British
COUNTRY: U.S.A.
MANUFACTURER: Savage Arms Corp. U.S.A.
CYCLIC RATE OF FIRE: 500 rpm
SYSTEM OF OPERATION(S): gas
TYPE OF FIRE: full auto only
AMMUNITION DELIVERY BY: 47- or 96-round drum magazine
SERIAL NO.: 14327

COMMENTS: This gun came from the Arizona National Guard Museum. Originally it had been ordered by the famous Mexican bandit Pancho Villa. Villa purchased this firearm with three others from T.F. Miller Hardware Co. in Clarkdale, Arizona where Villa had at one time been employed. The guns were being shipped to him for a Nogales, Mexico pickup and were intercepted by the U.S. Cavalry and detained by them. The Army eventually put them in storage and prior to WWI they were delivered to a military base and eventually found their way to Williams Field where they served as guard guns during WWII. Later two of them went to the Arizona National Guard, one to the Mesa Police Department and one to the Phoenix Police Department. This speciman was one of those given to the Arizona National Guard and later acquired by Earl. It is shown in its original packing crate and was complete with several 47-round magazines of original 1916 ammunition when captured. Mr. Earl test-fired the gun approximately 100 rounds and put it into his collection and it has not been fired since that time. It is an "as new", mint gun—a very rare and a desirable collector's piece.

NAME: BAR (Browning Light Machine Rifle)
MODEL: 1918
CALIBER: .30-1906
COUNTRY: U.S.A.
MANUFACTURER: Colt, Winchester, Marlin, Rockwell
CYCLIC RATE OF FIRE: 500 rpm
SYSTEM OF OPERATION(S): gas
TYPE OF FIRE: selective
AMMUNITION DELIVERY BY: 20-round staggered cartridge magazine
SERIAL NO.: 100206

COMMENTS: Another of John M. Browning's famous invention, the Browning Automatic Rifle was designed to be used by an individual soldier who could use aimed single shots or, at the touch of a switch, full automatic fire. Browning's genius put this gun into use in WWI where it gained favorable approval by the American Expeditionary Forces in Europe. Its accuracy, dependability and reliability in the field was exceptional. The BAR has seen continuous use from 1918 through Korea, being supplemented by the 19A2 revised model. Note the high quality of the workmanship on this firearm: the high-gloss finish and the carefully-carved and beautifully-finished wood and furnishings on the gun showing truly old world pride of workmanship. The BAR enjoyed wide popularity of military organization all over the world. This particular specimen is brand new and unfired.

NAME: Lewis Aircraft Light Machine Gun
MODEL: 1917-18
CALIBER: .30-1906
COUNTRY: U.S.A.
MANUFACTURER: Savage Arms Corp.
CYCLIC RATE OF FIRE: 600-650 rpm
SYSTEM OF OPERATION(S): gas
TYPE OF FIRE: full auto only
AMMUNITION DELIVERY BY: 97-round drum magazine
SERIAL NO.: 20343

COMMENTS: Credit should be given to Col. Isaac N. Lewis of the U.S. Army for design of the firearm as well as his refusal to accept any royalty payments from the U.S. Government for his services. This specimen has a rare half jacket to protect the barrel.

NAME: Lewis Aircraft Light Machine Gun
MODEL: 1917-18
CALIBER: .30-1906
COUNTRY: U.S.A.
MANUFACTURER: Savage Arms Corp.
CYCLIC RATE OF FIRE: 600-650 rpm
SYSTEM OF OPERATION(S): gas
TYPE OF FIRE: full auto only
AMMUNITION DELIVERY BY: 97-round drum magazine
SERIAL NO.: 57835

COMMENTS: The Lewis was one of the most important aircraft machine guns used in WWI and was used through WWII. The versatility of the Lewis Gun is unchallenged. It could be mounted on the wing of an aircraft for forward firing and equally as well in a ring mount for the observer to protect the rear of the airplane. It was also used in many instances in dual and blister mounts on bombers. The reliability, light weight, and versatility of the gun made it one of this century's greatest military inventions.

NAME: Marlin Aircraft Machine Gun
MODEL: 1917
CALIBER: .30-1906
COUNTRY: U.S.A.
MANUFACTURER: Marlin Firearms Co., U.S.A.
CYCLIC RATE OF FIRE: 630 rpm
SYSTEM OF OPERATION(S): gas
TYPE OF FIRE: full auto only
AMMUNITION DELIVERY BY: fabric web belt
SERIAL NO.: 34898

COMMENTS: This cowl-mounted Marlin gun was found on a fighter aircraft late in WWI. It slowly replaced the heavier and larger Vickers, as it provided a slight edge of fire power by delivering a faster cyclic rate. After the war the Marlin aircraft machine gun became the U.S. Army Air Force's primary forward-firing weapon. It was eventually replaced by the Browning AN-M2. The large bulge on the top of the receiver is the synchronizing mechanism which was attached by linkage to the engine which prevented the guns firing into the propeller.

NAME: Vickers Aircraft Machine Gun
MODEL: Mark 1
CALIBER: 11mm
COUNTRY: Britain
MANUFACTURER: various United Kingdom arsenals
CYCLIC RATE OF FIRE: 550 rpm
SYSTEM OF OPERATION(S): recoil
TYPE OF FIRE: full auto only
AMMUNITION DELIVERY BY: fabric web belt
SERIAL NO.: 945, A1646, A2001

COMMENTS: This Vickers gun is fitted with its top-mounted engine synchronizer bar to prevent shots striking the propeller of the aircraft. It is also equipped with a small flash suppressor scoop under the muzzle. This is the type most commonly found mounted on S.P.A.D.s and *Camel* fighter aircraft. These guns were equipped with a remote firing cable with a trigger affixed to the pilot's joy stick. The Vickers was commonly used in single or dual mounts. This gun is 11mm caliber, which was designed as a "balloon buster" cartridge. The 11mm was large enough to insert a small amount of gun powder in the base of the bullet, so the bullet tended to ignite the hydrogen-filled balloons, bringing them down in flames. It was also found to be far more effective in air-to-air combat than the .303 cartridge. After WWI Vickers continued to be used by all of the allied countries but were subsequently phased out in preference to lighter and faster-firing guns.

NAME: Owen
MODEL: MK 1
CALIBER: 9mm
COUNTRY: Australia
MANUFACTURER: Lysaghts Newcastle Works
CYCLIC RATE OF FIRE: 700 rpm
SYSTEM OF OPERATION(S): blowback
TYPE OF FIRE: full auto
AMMUNITION DELIVERY BY: 33-round box magazine
SERIAL NO.: 9521

COMMENTS: Since Britain could not supply enough Sten guns the Australians designed two submachine guns of their own, the Austen and Owen. The latter was far more reliable and robust for the jungle, and was more popular with the troops.

NAME: Lanchester
MODEL: MK 1
CALIBER: 9mm
COUNTRY: Great Britain
MANUFACTURER: Sterling Armament Co.
CYCLIC RATE OF FIRE: 600 rpm
SYSTEM OF OPERATION(S): blowback
TYPE OF FIRE: selective
AMMUNITION DELIVERY BY: 50-round magazine
SERIAL NO.: 24316A

COMMENTS: The British designer, Lanchester, copied the successful German designed MP 28/II. First produced in 1941, the Lanchester stayed in Royal Navy service until replaced in the early 1960s.

NAME: Sten
MODEL: MK 2
CALIBER: 9mm
COUNTRY: Great Britain
MANUFACTURER: BSA and other Royal Ordnance Factories
CYCLIC RATE OF FIRE: 550 rpm
SYSTEM OF OPERATION(S): blowback
TYPE OF FIRE: automatic
AMMUNITION DELIVERY BY: 32-round box magazine
SERIAL NO.: FP77286

COMMENTS: Conceived in 1941 at the Royal Small Arms at Enfield, more than four million would be produced by 1945. Cheapness and simplicity were paramount in the design, and, despite some shortcomings, mainly in the single-feed magazine, the Sten was one of the outstanding designs of WWII.

NAME: Sten
MODEL: MK 3
CALIBER: 9mm
COUNTRY: Great Britain
MANUFACTURER: BSA and other Royal Ordnance Factories
CYCLIC RATE OF FIRE: 550 rpm
SYSTEM OF OPERATION(S): blowback
TYPE OF FIRE: automatic
AMMUNITION DELIVERY BY: 32-round box magazine
SERIAL NO.: F-90043

COMMENTS: The MK 3 was the second of the Sten series to be made in large numbers and, with the MK 2, is the one which was most frequently found in British service. Other variations included the MK 4 and 5.

NAME: British Aircraft Machine Gun
MODEL: MK 2
CALIBER: .303 British
COUNTRY: England
MANUFACTURER: BSA, United Kingdom
CYCLIC RATE OF FIRE: 1000 rpm
SYSTEM OF OPERATION(S): recoil
TYPE OF FIRE: full auto only
AMMUNITION DELIVERY BY: disintegrating steel link belt
SERIAL NO.: 116671

COMMENTS: This is another example of the American gun inventor John M. Browning's genius in his development of the AN-M2, of which this MK 2 model is an exact copy other than the caliber. During WWII Britain was given manufacturing rights to manufacture the MK 2 for their own use. Many MK 2 machine guns were used as free or swivel guns in aircraft and they also found wide usage in multiple gun turret mountings.

NAME: Bren
MODEL: MK 1
CALIBER: .303
COUNTRY: Great Britain
MANUFACTURER: Royal Small Arms Factory at Enfield
CYCLIC RATE OF FIRE: 500 rpm
SYSTEM OF OPERATION(S): gas
TYPE OF FIRE: full auto
AMMUNITION DELIVERY BY: 30-round box magazine
SERIAL NO.: V 299

COMMENTS: The British Army began searching for a replacement for the Lewis gun in the early 1930s. Specimens of the Czech 2B26 were tested and because of its fine performance was immediately accepted with the .303 cartridge being substituted for the 2B26's 7.92mm. First produced in 1937, the Bren Gun without a doubt is one of the finest light machine guns ever devised.

NAME: Bren
MODEL: L 4
CALIBER: 7.92mm
COUNTRY: Great Britain (Chinese Nationalist Contract)
MANUFACTURER: Canadian Armory
CYCLIC RATE OF FIRE: 500 rpm
SYSTEM OF OPERATION(S): gas
TYPE OF FIRE: full auto
AMMUNITION DELIVERY BY: 30-round box magazine
SERIAL NO.: CH9629

COMMENTS: Post-WWII development of the combat-proven Bren gun continued with many improvements, including conversion from .303 cartridge to the NATO 7.92mm cartridge. The Canadian Armories delivered several thousand of this version to the Nationalist Chinese, one of which is seen here.

NAME: Bren
MODEL: MK 2
CALIBER: .303
COUNTRY: Great Britain
MANUFACTURER: initially at the Royal Small Arms at Enfield and later in Canadian Ordnance Factories
CYCLIC RATE OF FIRE: 500 rpm
SYSTEM OF OPERATION(S): gas
TYPE OF FIRE:
AMMUNITION DELIVERY BY: 30-round box magazine
SERIAL NO.: 14T2185

COMMENTS: Staying with the excellent design of 1937, the MK 2 was put into production in 1942. Certain modifications to the receiver, stock, and sights were made for ease of productions.

NAME: ZB, Brno
MODEL: 26
CALIBER: 7.92mm
COUNTRY: Czechoslovakia
MANUFACTURER: ZB
CYCLIC RATE OF FIRE: 500 rpm
SYSTEM OF OPERATION(S): gas
TYPE OF FIRE: full auto
AMMUNITION DELIVERY BY: 30-round box magazine
SERIAL NO.: 0399

COMMENTS: The Czech armament firm commonly known as ZB was formed after WWI and the ZB-26 was their first design. Far superior in design features and materials, it was an immediate success and was the model for many other designs including the famous British Bren gun.

NAME: Chatellerault
MODEL: 1924/29
CALIBER: 7.5mm
COUNTRY: France
MANUFACTURER: MAS
CYCLIC RATE OF FIRE: 500 rpm
SYSTEM OF OPERATION(S): gas
TYPE OF FIRE: selective
AMMUNITION DELIVERY BY: 25-round box magazine
SERIAL NO.: C19943

COMMENTS: Quickly replacing the infamous Chauchat design of WWI, the French adopted the Chatellerault light machine gun based on the combat proven Browning Automatic Rifle. The gun was used by the French in armored vehicles and the Maginot Line defenses. The Germans also used captured Chatelleraults in their Normandy fixed defenses.

NAME: Hotchkiss
MODEL: 1924 (Light)
CALIBER: various calibers
COUNTRY: France
MANUFACTURER: various French armories
CYCLIC RATE OF FIRE: 450 rpm
SYSTEM OF OPERATION(S): gas
TYPE OF FIRE: full auto
AMMUNITION DELIVERY BY: 25-round strip feed
SERIAL NO.: E 20839

COMMENTS: Offered in the post-WWI era, the French found little acceptance of the 1924 Hotchkiss. It was bought by several countries, but never enjoyed a commercial success.

NAME: French Aircraft Machine Gun
MODEL: 1931 Aircraft
CALIBER: 7.5mm
COUNTRY: France
MANUFACTURER: The Darne Co., France
CYCLIC RATE OF FIRE: 1200-1700 rpm
SYSTEM OF OPERATION(S): gas
TYPE OF FIRE: full auto only
AMMUNITION DELIVERY BY: steel belt link
SERIAL NO.: 6947

COMMENTS: The Darne is rather rough in appearance but is unique in many factors. The French considered ease of manufacture primary to cosmetics and design. Even though the Darne employed many complicated mechanical features, the superior cyclic rate gave it a substantial advantage over other slow-firing aircraft guns in WWII.

NAME: MAS
MODEL: M-38
CALIBER: 7.65mm
COUNTRY: France
MANUFACTURER: MAS, Saint-Etienne
CYCLIC RATE OF FIRE: 600 rpm
SYSTEM OF OPERATION(S): blowback
TYPE OF FIRE: full auto
AMMUNITION DELIVERY BY: 32-round box magazine
SERIAL NO.: F23136

COMMENTS: First produced in 1938, the MAS 38 was well made and an advanced design for its period. Unfortunately, it was not made in the 9mm Parabellum, the common submachine gun caliber in Europe, and was therefore never accepted by any other country.

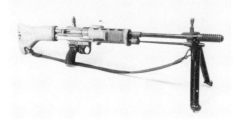

NAME: FG-42
MODEL: 1942
CALIBER: 7.92mm
COUNTRY: Germany
MANUFACTURER: Rheinmetall - Borsig AG
CYCLIC RATE OF FIRE: 750 rpm
SYSTEM OF OPERATION(S): gas
TYPE OF FIRE: selective
AMMUNITION DELIVERY BY: 20-round box magazine
SERIAL NO.: 04071

COMMENTS: One of the outstanding designs of WWII, the FG-42 was only produced for the German paratroops because of its high manufacturing cost. Only 7,000 were produced, but it was a forerunner of the modern assault rifle. It fires from an open breech for automatic fire to help cooling, but from a closed breech in semi-auto to increase accuracy. Only a handful remain in existence.

NAME: MP-44
MODEL: Krummlauf
CALIBER: 7.92mm
COUNTRY: Germany
MANUFACTURER: Haenel Waffen
CYCLIC RATE OF FIRE: 500 rpm
SYSTEM OF OPERATION(S): gas
TYPE OF FIRE: selective
AMMUNITION DELIVERY BY: 30-round box magazine
SERIAL NO.: 254 h/44

COMMENTS: The MP-44 (or StG-44) was fitted with mirror sights and a curved barrel to:
• fire around a corner?
• dislodge belligerent Russians from inside tanks?
• designed from a test program to find a use in the field with no specific purpose in mind?
Although never successful, it is a rare piece of German technology.

NAME: StG-44
MODEL: 1944
CALIBER: 7.92mm
COUNTRY: Germany
MANUFACTURER: Haenel Waffen
CYCLIC RATE OF FIRE: 500 rpm
SYSTEM OF OPERATION(S): gas
TYPE OF FIRE: selective
AMMUNITION DELIVERY BY: 30-round box magazine
SERIAL NO.: 7154 y/45

COMMENTS: The final version of a line of rifles designed by Schmeisser, the StG-44 was one of the first uncomplicated and cheaply-made assault rifles and was very successful in its role.

NAME: MG-34
MODEL: n/a
CALIBER: 7.92mm
COUNTRY: Germany
MANUFACTURER: Mauser and others
CYCLIC RATE OF FIRE: 800-900 rpm
SYSTEM OF OPERATION(S): short recoil
TYPE OF FIRE: selective and full auto
AMMUNITION DELIVERY BY: metal linked belt
SERIAL NO.: 4125i

COMMENTS: This specimen is shown in the heavy machine gun role with the Lafelle 34 mount.

NAME: MG-34
MODEL: n/a
CALIBER: 7.92mm
COUNTRY: Germany
MANUFACTURER: Mauser and others
CYCLIC RATE OF FIRE: 800-900 rpm
SYSTEM OF OPERATION(S): short recoil
TYPE OF FIRE: selective
AMMUNITION DELIVERY BY: metal linked belt
SERIAL NO.: 468d

COMMENTS: The MG-34 was introduced into the German Army in 1936. It was a radical design in that it was the first machine gun to serve multi-purpose missions, i.e., light, heavy, anti-aircraft and vehicle adaptations. Also it was one of the first light guns to use a belt feed. However, the MG-34 was costly in time and materials to manufacture and was replaced by the MG-42 in 1943. This specimen is shown in the light machine gun role with a bipod and anti-aircraft mount.

NAME: MG-34
MODEL: n/a
CALIBER: 7.92mm
COUNTRY: Germany
MANUFACTURER: Mauser and others
CYCLIC RATE OF FIRE: 800-900 rpm
SYSTEM OF OPERATION(S): short recoil
TYPE OF FIRE: selective and full auto
AMMUNITION DELIVERY BY: metal linked belt
SERIAL NO.: 9619a

COMMENTS: This specimen was utilized in vehicle and armor mountings.

NAME: MG-42
MODEL: n/a
CALIBER: 7.62 NATO
COUNTRY: W. Germany
MANUFACTURER: Rheinmetall
CYCLIC RATE OF FIRE: 750-1350 rpm depending on modifications
SYSTEM OF OPERATION(S): short recoil
TYPE OF FIRE: selective
AMMUNITION DELIVERY BY: linked metal belt
SERIAL NO.: 2590J

COMMENTS: This specimen is shown in its heavy machine gun role with appropriate mount.

NAME: MG-42
MODEL: n/a
CALIBER: 7.92mm
COUNTRY: Germany
MANUFACTURER: Mauser and others
CYCLIC RATE OF FIRE: 1200 rpm
SYSTEM OF OPERATION(S): short recoil
TYPE OF FIRE: selective
AMMUNITION DELIVERY BY: metal linked belt
SERIAL NO.: 7392

COMMENTS: Facing a critical shortage of MG-34s, in 1941 the Germans designed and adopted the MG-42. It was also a multi-purpose machine gun, but was far easier to manufacture and had several advantages over the 34. Barrel changes could be made in seconds and it had a cyclic rate of 1200 rpm. More reliable than the MG-34, it also was more resistant to dirt and jamming. This specimen is shown in its light machine gun role with a bipod.

NAME: Schnellfeuer
MODEL: M-30 (M712)
CALIBER: 7.63mm
COUNTRY: Germany
MANUFACTURER: Mauser
CYCLIC RATE OF FIRE: n/a
SYSTEM OF OPERATION(S): blowback
TYPE OF FIRE: selective
AMMUNITION DELIVERY BY: clip
SERIAL NO.: 13210

COMMENTS: The full-automatic Mauser pistol and stock were produced in 1931 and 1000 went to China. Its high rate of fire made the gun unmanageable, thereby never becoming a commercial or military success in its full automatic role.

NAME: MP-28/II
MODEL: MP-28/II
CALIBER: 9mm
COUNTRY: Germany
MANUFACTURER: Haenel
CYCLIC RATE OF FIRE: 500 rpm
SYSTEM OF OPERATION(S): blowback
TYPE OF FIRE: selective
AMMUNITION DELIVERY BY: 20-, 32- or 50-round box magazine
SERIAL NO.: 15320

COMMENTS: Apart from several modifications, the MP-28/II was a direct descendant of the MP-18/1. The main difference was a selector for semi-automatic fire. The gun was a commercial success in the 1930s and its popularity in the Spanish Civil War started the rush for other countries to develop a similar gun.

NAME: Solothurn
MODEL: MP S1-100 (Steyr-Solothurn)
CALIBER: 9mm
COUNTRY: Switzerland and Austria
MANUFACTURER: Waffenfabrik Solothurn AG
CYLIC RATE OF FIRE: 500 rpm
SYSTEM OF OPERATION(S): blowback
TYPE OF FIRE: full auto
AMMUNITION DELIVERY BY: 32-round box magazine
SERIAL NO.: 5693

COMMENTS: The Solothurn was widely issued to German troops in WWII and many thought it was made in Germany. However, it was produced in Switzerland by Solothurn (owned then by the German company Rheinmetall) and also produced in Steyr, Austria. Both versions were beautifully made from machined parts, and the Steyr-Solothurn is a departure from the mass-produced steel stamped guns of a later generation.

NAME: EMP (Erma Machine Pistol)
MODEL: EMP
CALIBER: 9mm
COUNTRY: Germany
MANUFACTURER: Erma
CYCLIC RATE OF FIRE: 500 rpm
SYSTEM OF OPERATION(S): blowback
TYPE OF FIRE: full auto
AMMUNITION DELIVERY BY: 25- or 32-round box magazine
SERIAL NO.: 10463

COMMENTS: The EMP was produced from 1930-1938 and was unique in that the bolt, firing pin, and return spring were housed in a tubular telescoping casing, making it easy to disassemble and free of dirt. First production went to the Yugoslavian Army, the Paraguayan and Bolivian Armies in the Chaco War of 1932-35 and eventually supplied the German Army until 1942.

NAME: Bergmann
MODEL: MP-35/1
CALIBER: 9mm
COUNTRY: Germany
MANUFACTURER: Junker & Ruh
CYCLIC RATE OF FIRE: 650 rpm
SYSTEM OF OPERATION(S): blowback
TYPE OF FIRE: selective
AMMUNITION DELIVERY BY: 24- or 32-round box
  magazine
SERIAL NO.: 1926/C

COMMENTS: The MP-35/1 was the military version of the commercial MP-34/1. Manufactured under license by Junker & Ruh, it was the standard sub-machine gun of the Waffen SS. The bolt handle was peculiar as it had to be rotated and pulled back to retract the bolt. Thus, the handle was stationary when firing and there was no bolt slot for dirt to enter.

NAME: MP-38 (Schmeisser)
MODEL: MP-38
CALIBER: 9mm
COUNTRY: Germany
MANUFACTURER: Erma
CYCLIC RATE OF FIRE: 500 rpm
SYSTEM OF OPERATION(S): blowback
TYPE OF FIRE: full auto
AMMUNITION DELIVERY BY: 32-round box
  magazine
SERIAL NO.: 2065a

COMMENTS: Although commonly called the Schmeisser, Hugo Schmeisser had nothing to do with development of the MP-38. This is probably the most famous military sub-machine gun to be adopted by a major army. It was first to use all metal and plastic, first to use a folding stock and first to be used by a fast-moving mechanized army.

NAME: MP-38/40 (Schmeisser)
MODEL: MP-38/40
CALIBER: 9mm
COUNTRY: Germany
MANUFACTURER: Erma and other German
  manufacturers
CYCLIC RATE OF FIRE: 500 rpm
SYSTEM OF OPERATION(S): blowback
TYPE OF FIRE: full auto
AMMUNITION DELIVERY BY: 32-round box
  magazine
SERIAL NO.: 5264

COMMENTS: The MP-38 was an excellent sub-machine gun, but was expensive to manufacture. Therefore, stamped steel parts and other modifications were introduced to reduce fabrication in time and materials. Many MP-38s were modified to the MP-38/40 as this example.

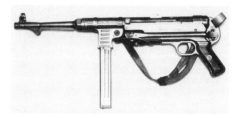

NAME: MP-40 (Schmeisser)
MODEL: MP-40
CALIBER: 9mm
COUNTRY: Germany
MANUFACTURER: Erma, Haenel, and Steyr
CYCLIC RATE OF FIRE: 500 rpm
SYSTEM OF OPERATION(S): blowback
TYPE OF FIRE: full auto
AMMUNITION DELIVERY BY: 32-round box
  magazine
SERIAL NO.: 30869

COMMENTS: The MP-40 was substantially the same as the MP-38 but its construction utilized a minimum of machine operations and a maximum of subassemblies sub-contracted to minor firms throughout Germany.

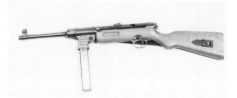

NAME: MP-41 (Schmeisser)
MODEL: MP-41
CALIBER: 9mm
COUNTRY: Germany
MANUFACTURER: Erma
CYCLIC RATE OF FIRE: 500 rpm
SYSTEM OF OPERATION(S): blowback
TYPE OF FIRE: full auto
AMMUNITION DELIVERY BY: 32-round box
  magazine
SERIAL NO.: 26570

COMMENTS: A wooden-stock gun based on the MP-40 was developed in 1941, but it was a step backwards and not a success. This example is documented as having been found in the Berlin bunker of Adolf Hitler during the last days of WWII.

NAME: Toy Submachine Gun
MODEL: MP-40
SERIAL NO.: N/A

COMMENTS: Nothing is known about the background of this blank-firing MP-40 two-thirds scale replica, except that is was puchased by Champlin from a collector of German toys. It may be German. It is shown here with a variant of the gun from which it was modeled. Whoever built it had great reverence for the original, for even some of the cast and formed parts have been painstakingly finished to duplicate the German original's appearance.

NAME: German Aircraft Machine Gun
MODEL: MG-15
CALIBER: 7.92mm
COUNTRY: Germany
MANUFACTURER: Rheinmetall-Borsig A.G.,
  Germany
CYCLIC RATE OF FIRE: 1000 rpm
SYSTEM OF OPERATION(S): recoil
TYPE OF FIRE: full auto only
AMMUNITION DELIVERY BY: 75-round dual drum
  magazine
SERIAL NO.: 31940-41

COMMENTS: This very efficient light aircraft machine gun was employed on many of Germany's bombers as primary aircraft armament. Its double drum magazine is unusual and feeds one cartridge from each drum by means of spring-loaded tension. Empty magazines can be replaced in a matter of seconds. The larger aircraft employing this weapon were supplied with kits consisting of a butt stock and a snap-on barrel shroud which contained a bipod and ground firing sights. This was for crew use in case they desired to remove the gun and employ it as a ground mount.

NAME: German Aircraft Machine Gun
MODEL: MG-17
CALIBER: 7.92mm
COUNTRY: Germany
MANUFACTURER: Rheinmetall-Borsig A.G.,
  Germany
CYCLIC RATE OF FIRE: 1000 rpm synchronized or
  1100 rpm unsynchronized
SYSTEM OF OPERATION(S): recoil
TYPE OF FIRE: full auto only
AMMUNITION DELIVERY BY: continuous steel link
  belt
SERIAL NO.: 4032627

COMMENTS: The MG-17 is the end result of Rheinmetall redesigning the MG-15 in an effort to produce a fast-firing gun employing remote-control operation. This gun was designed for hydraulic charging and electric sylinoid firing control. It was usually employed in dual mounts in the nose of fighter aircraft. It was also employed as a fixed gun firing rearward from the tail in some light bombers.

NAME: German Oerlikon Aircraft Cannon
MODEL: MG-FFM
CALIBER: 20mm
COUNTRY: Germany
MANUFACTURER: Rheinmetall, Germany
CYCLIC RATE OF FIRE: 550 rpm
SYSTEM OF OPERATION(S): recoil
TYPE OF FIRE: full auto only
AMMUNITION DELIVERY BY: 60-round drum or continuous steel link belt
SERIAL NO.: 27199

COMMENTS: The Rheinmetall 20mm cannon was one of Germany's most successful aircraft weapons. It was used in all applications on their fighter aircraft and was only superceded late in the war by the 30mm. This cannon was based on the Oerlikon principle and was copied by the Germans from Switzerland early in the war. Many other countries including the U.S. also borrowed the Oerlikon principle and put it to use against the Germans. This machine-cannon exhibits extreme engineering skill and flawless German workmanship as can be readily seen looking at this specimen.

NAME: German Aircraft Machine Gun
MODEL: MG-81
CALIBER: 7.92mm
COUNTRY: Germany
MANUFACTURER: Hauser Werke A.G., Germany
CYCLIC RATE OF FIRE: 1200-1500 rpm
SYSTEM OF OPERATION(S): recoil
TYPE OF FIRE: full auto
AMMUNITION DELIVERY BY: disintegrating steel link belt
SERIAL NO.: 67523

COMMENTS: This very fine engineered light-weight aircraft gun was employed by the Germans as a primary defensive weapon protecting their aircraft. It was used in various gun ports located from nose to tail on most aircraft, and many times it was employed as a dual gun coupled together to fire in unison.

NAME: German Dual Aircraft Machine Gun
MODEL: MG81-Z
CALIBER: 7.92mm
COUNTRY: Germany
MANUFACTURER: Mauser Werke A.G., Germany
CYCLIC RATE OF FIRE: 2400-3000 rpm
SYSTEM OF OPERATION(S): recoil
TYPE OF FIRE: full auto only
AMMUNITION DELIVERY BY: disintegrating steel metal belt
SERIAL NO.: 40027 and 40038

COMMENTS: This machine gun in its dual configuration was one of the finest engineered and constructed weapons of its caliber in WWII. It had quick-change barrel capabilities and could be moved in and out of its aircraft mount in a matter of seconds. It is interesting to note that two of these guns could deliver the same firepower as one of our modern Vulcan miniguns firing on the Gatling principle.

NAME: German Aircraft Machine Gun
MODEL: MG-131
CALIBER: 13mm
COUNTRY: Germany
MANUFACTURER: Rheinmetall-Borsig, A.G., Germany
CYCLIC RATE OF FIRE: 900 rpm
SYSTEM OF OPERATION(S): recoil
TYPE OF FIRE: full auto only
AMMUNITION DELIVERY BY: steel link belt
SERIAL NO.: NR-55968

COMMENTS: As development progressed in WWII, aircraft became faster and larger, necessitating larger calibers and faster-firing guns to bring them down. The MG-131 13mm gun was designed to replace or supplement the MG-17 then in use. Another advantage of the larger caliber was the diversification of loadings that could be used. This cartridge was also advanced in that it was not detonated by a spring-loaded firing pin, but rather by electricity which resulted in better synchronization and fire interruption control. Most MG-131s were used in fixed mountings, but many were also used as flexible or free guns and multiple turret mountings. This particular MG-131 was a souvenir taken from the nose of a ME-109 shot down over England.

NAME: German Aircraft Machine Cannon
MODEL: MK-108
CALIBER: 30mm
COUNTRY: Germany
MANUFACTURER: Rheinmetall-Borsig, Germany
CYCLIC RATE OF FIRE: 450 rpm
SYSTEM OF OPERATION(S): recoil, blowback
TYPE OF FIRE: full auto only
AMMUNITION DELIVERY BY: disintegrating steel metal link belts
SERIAL NO.: 24939

COMMENTS: Germany's sole purpose for developing this large caliber machine cannon was for use against Allied heavy bombers. Designed in 1941 it went into high priority production in 1944. Rheinmetall installed it in such fighter aircraft as the ME-109, 190's, 262 jet fighter, and the 163 rocket interceptor. It is generally accepted that just one hit in any of its critical locations from this large caliber explosive cannon shell was sufficient to bring down the largest bomber. This MK-108 30mm machine cannon is the only one of its kind known in the U.S. in a private collection.

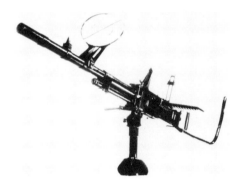

NAME: Breda
MODEL: M-37
CALIBER: 8mm
COUNTRY: Italy
MANUFACTURER: Breda
CYCLIC RATE OF FIRE: 450 rpm
SYSTEM OF OPERATION(S): gas
TYPE OF FIRE: full auto
AMMUNITION DELIVERY BY: 20-round strip magazine
SERIAL NO.: 161

COMMENTS: The M-37 was the standard Italian Army WWII machine gun. Although fairly conventional in design, it had a major drawback in that it had to oil the spent cartridge hulls before extraction, and the tray feeding system was complicated and time consuming to reload.

NAME: Beretta
MODEL: MP38A
CALIBER: 9mm
COUNTRY: Italy
MANUFACTURER: Pietro Beretta Spa
CYCLIC RATE OF FIRE: 600 rpm
SYSTEM OF OPERATION(S): blowback
TYPE OF FIRE: selective
AMMUNITION DELIVERY BY: 10-, 20-, 30- or 40-round box magazine
SERIAL NO.: 3135

COMMENTS: An excellent design, the Model 38A was well made and long lasting for a sub-machine gun. It equipped the Italian Army in WWII and was supplied to German and Rumanian units also. A special high-velocity 9mm cartridge was later developed which gave it longer range.

NAME: Beretta
MODEL: MP 38/42
CALIBER: 9mm
COUNTRY: Italy
MANUFACTURER: Pietro Beretta Spa
CYCLIC RATE OF FIRE: 550 rpm
SYSTEM OF OPERATION(S): blowback
TYPE OF FIRE: selective
AMMUNITION DELIVERY BY: 20- or 40-round box magazine
SERIAL NO.: 4362

COMMENTS: The Model 38/42 was a wartime product which was less expensive and easier to produce than the MP 38A. Despite the modifications, the 38/42 was still made to high standards and Beretta returned to producing the gun in the standard 9mm Parabellum pistol cartridge. Besides the Italian Army, German and Rumanian units were supplied with the MP 38/42.

NAME: Breda
MODEL: M-30
CALIBER: 6.5mm
COUNTRY: Italy (Costa Rican Contract)
MANUFACTURER: Breda
CYCLIC RATE OF FIRE: 475 rpm
SYSTEM OF OPERATION(S): blowback
TYPE OF FIRE: full auto
AMMUNITION DELIVERY BY: 20-round box
SERIAL NO.: 48

COMMENTS: The M-30 was adopted by the Italian Army in 1930. Unfortunately, the gun had several major faults and was never popular. Its rate of fire was slow due to the difficulty in loading. Any damage to the magazine would put the gun out of action. However, some were sold commercially to Central and South American countries.

NAME: Breda
MODEL: M-30
CALIBER: 6.5mm
COUNTRY: Italy
MANUFACTURER: Breda Spa
CYCLIC RATE OF FIRE: 475 rpm
SYSTEM OF OPERATION(S): blowback
TYPE OF FIRE: full auto
AMMUNITION DELIVERY BY: 20-round box
SERIAL NO.: 43172

COMMENTS: The M-30 was adopted by the Italian Army in 1930. Unfortunately the gun had several major faults and was never a popular gun. Its rate of fire was slow due to the difficulty in loading and any damage to the magazine would put the gun out of action. However, some were sold commercially to Central and South American countries.

NAME: Japanese Sub-machine Gun
MODEL: Type 100
CALIBER: 8mm
COUNTRY: Japan
MANUFACTURER: State
CYCLIC RATE OF FIRE: 450 rpm
SYSTEM OF OPERATION(S): recoil
TYPE OF FIRE: full auto only
AMMUNITION DELIVERY BY: 30-round staggered box magazine
SERIAL NO.: 2726

COMMENTS: This is one of the rare sub-machine guns of the world and it is highly desired by all collectors of military automatics due to its scarcity and unique design. Though crudely made, it is an efficient sub-machine gun. Only three or four are known to exist.

NAME: Japanese Heavy Machine Gun
MODEL: Type 92
CALIBER: 7.7mm
COUNTRY: Japan
MANUFACTURER: Tokyo Arsenal
CYCLIC RATE OF FIRE: 450 rpm
SYSTEM OF OPERATION(S): gas
TYPE OF FIRE: full auto only
AMMUNITION DELIVERY BY: 30-round stripper clip
SERIAL NO.: 27536

COMMENTS: This Type 92 was acquired by Curtis Earl for his collection in 1981. It was captured by the First Marine Division on Bloody Ridge on Guadalcanal. During an inspection tour of Guadalcanal in November 1942, the gun was presented to Admiral "Bull" Halsey from General Vandegrift as a momento of the fighting that had occurred there. Later Admiral Halsey presented the gun to his Flag Secretary, Rear Admiral Nickol. Curtis Earl purchased the gun from Rear Admiral Nickol's son in 1981.

NAME: Japanese Heavy Machine Gun
MODEL: Type 92
CALIBER: 7.7mm
COUNTRY: Japan
MANUFACTURER: Tokyo Arsenal
CYCLIC RATE OF FIRE: 450 rpm
SYSTEM OF OPERATION(S): gas
TYPE OF FIRE: full auto only
AMMUNITION DELIVERY BY: 30-round stripper clip
SERIAL NO.: 340307

COMMENTS: This Japanese Type 92 Heavy Machine Gun was originally acquired by the Curtis Earl Collection from the Arizona National Guard Museum in 1968. The gun is almost an identical copy to the French Model 1914 Hotchkiss Machine Gun. It is very well made and in many ways exceeds the quality of the French gun it copied.

NAME: Japanese Light Machine Gun
MODEL: Type-11
CALIBER: 6.5mm
COUNTRY: Japan
MANUFACTURER: State Arsenal
CYCLIC RATE OF FIRE: 500 rpm
SYSTEM OF OPERATION(S): gas
TYPE OF FIRE: full auto only
AMMUNITION DELIVERY BY: 300-round hopper
SERIAL NO.: 68017

COMMENTS: The 11 Nen Shiki Kikanju was brought into service in 1922 as the first light machine gun the Japanese had designed themselves. The most unusual feature was its feed system in which a hopper on the left of the gun accepted clips for the Meiji 38 infantry rifle, stripped the rounds out and fed them into the breech. Thus any rifleman could provide ammunition for the gun.

NAME: Japanese Tank Machine Gun
MODEL: Type 97
CALIBER: 7.7mm
COUNTRY: Japan
MANUFACTURER: State Arsenal
CYCLIC RATE OF FIRE: 500 rpm
SYSTEM OF OPERATION(S): gas
TYPE OF FIRE: full auto only
AMMUNITION DELIVERY BY: staggered box magazine
SERIAL NO.: 15968

COMMENTS: This Type 97 Japanese Tanker Machine Gun is a copy of the Czech 26 employing the same internal parts and 30-round box magazine. It has a fold-around butt stock which was incorporated in its design to be used in cramped tank corridors, and was originally furnished with a telescope sight which is missing with this specimen.

NAME: Japanese Training Machine Gun
MODEL: Training
CALIBER: 6.5mm
COUNTRY: Japan
MANUFACTURER: Tokyo Arsenal
CYCLIC RATE OF FIRE: 500 rpm
SYSTEM OF OPERATION(S): recoil
TYPE OF FIRE: full auto only
AMMUNITION DELIVERY BY: single stacked box magazine, 20-round capacity
SERIAL NO.: 2594

COMMENTS: Same as above.

NAME: Japanese Light Machine Gun
MODEL: Type 96
CALIBER: 6.5mm
COUNTRY: Japan
MANUFACTURER: Tokyo Arsenal
CYCLIC RATE OF FIRE: 550 rpm
SYSTEM OF OPERATION(S): gas
TYPE OF FIRE: full auto only
AMMUNITION DELIVERY BY: 30-round box
  magazine
SERIAL NO.: 6460

COMMENTS: The Japanese Type 96 Light Machine Gun was a very good and serviceable WWII weapon. It was supplied with a telescopic sight and fitted with a bayonet lug for use with the standard infantry Japanese bayonet. It is a close copy of the Bren Gun or the ZB26 and has a quick change barrel which can be exchanged for a fresh barrel in a matter of seconds. In WWII it proved itself to be a very efficient and reliable machine gun in the hands of the Japanese Imperial forces.

NAME: Japanese Light Machine Gun
MODEL: Type 99
CALIBER: 7.7mm
COUNTRY: Japan
MANUFACTURER: Tokyo Arsenal
CYCLIC RATE OF FIRE: 850 rpm
SYSTEM OF OPERATION(S): gas
TYPE OF FIRE: full auto only
AMMUNITION DELIVERY BY: 30-round box
  magazine
SERIAL NO.: 6849

COMMENTS: This Type 99 machine gun is fitted with a three-power telescope sight. The gun is also fitted with a bayonet lug that fits the standard Japanese infantry bayonet. The gun is a nearly exact copy of the British Bren or the Check ZB26. It is a very well made, reliable, and accurate weapon. Barrel changes can be made in a matter of seconds, and the gun can be field stripped for service very simply and without tools.

NAME: Japanese Aircraft Machine Gun
MODEL: 1932
CALIBER: 7.7mm
COUNTRY: Japan
MANUFACTURER: Tokyo Arsenal
CYCLIC RATE OF FIRE: 550-600 rpm
SYSTEM OF OPERATION(S): gas
TYPE OF FIRE: full auto only
AMMUNITION DELIVERY BY: 47- or 96-round
  drum magazine
SERIAL NO.: 1297

COMMENTS: This Japanese Lewis Gun is an exact copy of the British or American Lewis as designed by Isaac Lewis in 1912. This model was primarily used as a swivel gun in Japanese aircraft, where it was employed for offensive and defensive combat.

NAME: Japanese Light Machine Gun
MODEL: 1932
CALIBER: 7.7mm
COUNTRY: Japan
MANUFACTURER: Tokyo Arsenal
CYCLIC RATE OF FIRE: 550 rpm
SYSTEM OF OPERATION(S): gas
TYPE OF FIRE: full auto only
AMMUNITION DELIVERY BY: 47- or 96-round
  circular drum magazine
SERIAL NO.: 7365

COMMENTS: This gun is an exact copy of the British or American Lewis gun as designed by Isaac Lewis in 1912. The Japanese faithfully copied every item down to the finest detail, and used it extensively through WWII. The large jacket surrounding the barrel is for cooling purposes. During firing it creates venting action, sucking air across aluminum vains which are in contact with the barrel and thus cooling the weapon.

NAME: Japanese Aircraft Machine Gun
MODEL: Type 87
CALIBER: 7.7mm
COUNTRY: Japan
MANUFACTURER: State Arsenal
CYCLIC RATE OF FIRE: 600 rpm
SYSTEM OF OPERATION(S): gas
TYPE OF FIRE: full auto only
AMMUNITION DELIVERY BY: a flat circular drum
  magazine
SERIAL NO.: 1333

COMMENTS: This Type 87 is one of the rarest Japanese aircraft machine guns extant. Only three are known in collections in the U.S. The gun is unusual in that it is a close copy to the British Bren Gun. However, it employs a drum magazine similar to the Russian Degtyrev principle. The front sight is a self-adjusting vain for speed and elevation. This gives the gunner compensation for his aircraft's speed and movement while sighting at his target.

NAME: Japanese Aircraft Machine Gun
MODEL: Type 98
CALIBER: 7.7mm
COUNTRY: Japan
MANUFACTURER: Tokyo Arsenal
CYLIC RATE OF FIRE: 950 rpm
SYSTEM OF OPERATION(S): recoil
TYPE OF FIRE: full auto only
AMMUNITION DELIVERY BY: dual-feeding
  75-round drum
SERIAL NO.: 2021

COMMENTS: This aircraft machine gun was built under license from Rheinmetall-Borsig in Germany for the Japanese Imperial forces. It is an exact copy of the German MG-15 aircraft machine gun. This weapon saw wide usage by the Japanese in the Pacific in WWII.

NAME: Japanese Aircraft Machine Gun
MODEL: Type 89
CALIBER: 7.7mm
COUNTRY: Japan
MANUFACTURER: State Arsenal
CYCLIC RATE OF FIRE: 600 rpm
SYSTEM OF OPERATION(S): recoil
TYPE OF FIRE: full auto only
AMMUNITION DELIVERY BY: Fabric Web Belt
SERIAL NO.: 1065 ECC

COMMENTS: The 7.7mm Type 89 is almost an exact copy of the English Vickers Aircraft machine gun. It has been improved somewhat in that the cooling jacket is a smaller diameter. It was used primarily in fighter aircraft as a primary or spotter gun used to direct fire for the larger wing-mounted guns. However, it in itself was devastating when properly used. This Japanese Vickers was returned to the U.S. by a serviceman in the Pacific Theater, where he recovered it from the cowl mount of a shot-down Zero.

NAME: Japanese Aircraft Machine Gun
MODEL: Type 1941
CALIBER: 12.7mm
COUNTRY: Japan
MANUFACTURER: State Arsenal
CYCLIC RATE OF FIRE: 900 rpm
SYSTEM OF OPERATION(S): recoil
TYPE OF FIRE: full auto only
AMMUNITION DELIVERY BY: steel link belt
SERIAL NO.: 486

COMMENTS: This Japanese aircraft machine gun is almost an exact copy of the Browning .50 caliber M-2. The Japanese in WWII, not having a large gun of their own, copied the U.S. .50 caliber almost to the letter and used it successfully in their fighter aircraft. The Japanese employed a unique system in firing their guns. They would fire the 7mm cowl guns until they saw their tracers striking the target and then switch to 12.7mm guns. Only three of these 12.7mm Browning copy type 1941s are known to exist. This gun was recovered from a downed Zero fighter and sent home by the victorious pilot as a souvenir of WWII.

NAME: Russian Tank Machine Gun
MODEL: DT
CALIBER: 7.62mm
COUNTRY: U.S.S.R.
MANUFACTURER: unknown
CYCLIC RATE OF FIRE: 600 rpm
SYSTEM OF OPERATION(S): gas
TYPE OF FIRE: full auto only
AMMUNITION DELIVERY BY: 60-round drum
SERIAL NO.: 5028

COMMENTS: This model DT Tanker Machine Gun is rarely found in collections in the U.S. It is a very efficient and dependable gun, employing many unique features. It was especially serviceable in adverse weather conditions in which the Russians frequently fought.

NAME: Maxim
MODEL: 1910
CALIBER: 7.62mm
COUNTRY: U.S.S.R.
MANUFACTURER: State factories
CYCLIC RATE OF FIRE: 500 rpm
SYSTEM OF OPERATION(S): recoil operated
TYPE OF FIRE: full auto
AMMUNITION DELIVERY BY: belt fed
SERIAL NO.: HY21

COMMENTS: By 1910 the Russians were producing their own Maxim-designed heavy machine gun. It stayed in service throughout WWI and the Russian Revolution. It has continued to see usage in all Soviet satellites and reportedly still is seen in second-line service in several Eastern bloc countries. It is the longest lived of all the Maxim variants. This specimen was produced in the People's Republic of China.

NAME: Russian Light Machine Gun
MODEL: DP
CALIBER: 7.62mm
COUNTRY: U.S.S.R.
MANUFACTURER: State
CYCLIC RATE OF FIRE: 500-600 rpm
SYSTEM OF OPERATION(S): gas
TYPE OF FIRE: full auto only
AMMUNITION DELIVERY BY: 47-round drum
  magazine
SERIAL NO.: CB776

COMMENTS: This model DP Degtyaryov is a fine example of Soviet Russia's finest and most efficient WWII light machine gun. It is extremely simple, yet remarkably reliable and robust. It remained in service until the 1950s and many are in service today in Eastern Bloc countries and Asia.

NAME: Russian Sub-machine Gun
MODEL: PPSh 41
CALIBER: 7.62mm
COUNTRY: U.S.S.R.
MANUFACTURER: State
CYCLIC RATE OF FIRE: 900 rpm
SYSTEM OF OPERATION(S): recoil
TYPE OF FIRE: selective
AMMUNITION DELIVERY BY: 72-round drum or
  32-round box magazine
SERIAL NO.: B65390

COMMENTS: This PPSh 41 is a typical representative of the Soviet infantryman's sub-machine gun. About five million were issued in WWII, and accounted greatly toward the Russian victory. One of the gun's unique features is that it is made from one sheet of steel stamping formed to produce a complete receiver and barrel shroud. Even though it was not a beautifully furnished gun, it was nevertheless efficient, reliable, and highly accurate.

NAME: Russian Sub-machine Gun
MODEL: PPSh 41 (Kalashnikov)
CALIBER: 7.62mm
COUNTRY: U.S.S.R.
MANUFACTURER: State
CYCLIC RATE OF FIRE: 900 rpm
SYSTEM OF OPERATION(S): recoil
TYPE OF FIRE: selective
AMMUNITION DELIVERY BY: 72-round drum or
  35-round box magazine
SERIAL NO.: 354

COMMENTS: This PPSh 41 is unusual in that it was confiscated by the Las Vegas Police from a visiting Russian delegation in the 1960s.

NAME: Russian Sub-machine Gun
MODEL: PPS43
CALIBER: 7.62mm
COUNTRY: U.S.S.R.
MANUFACTURER: State
CYCLIC RATE OF FIRE: 700 rpm
SYSTEM OF OPERATION(S): recoil
TYPE OF FIRE: full auto only
AMMUNITION DELIVERY BY: 35-round magazine
SERIAL NO.: A14761

COMMENTS: This cheaply made, ingeniously designed stamped out sub-machine gun employs a fold over-the-top butt stock and muzzle compensator which assists in delivering accurate fire. The 43 gun was supposed to supplement the PPSh41, but after WWII approximately 1,000,000 had been produced, and they soon disappeared from Soviet inventories. This specimen was captured in Korea and brought home as a souvenir.

NAME: BAR (Browning Automatic Rifle)
MODEL: 1918-A2
CALIBER: .30-06
COUNTRY: U.S.A.
MANUFACTURER: Winchester
CYCLIC RATE OF FIRE: 2 speeds, switch
  controlled: 300-500 rpm
SYSTEM OF OPERATION(S): gas
TYPE OF FIRE: full auto only, 2 speeds adjustable
AMMUNITION DELIVERY BY: 20-rounds staggered
  cartridge magazine
SERIAL NO.: 16827

COMMENTS: This BAR is an early transition from the 1918 to the A-2 version with the dual-speed cyclic rate control. It was designed for the individual rifleman as a general-purpose assault weapon. It has been used by the U.S. in nearly all of its services and it has seen wide spread use throughout the world by NATO forces. It was our primary squad automatic weapon during the Korean War and saw wide usage in Vietnam and was, of course, one of our most popular weapons throughout WWII.

NAME: Colt Monitor BAR, Light Machine Rifle
MODEL: Colt Monitor
CALIBER: .30-06
COUNTRY: U.S.A.
MANUFACTURER: Colt Patent Fire Arms Co.
CYCLIC RATE OF FIRE: 500 rpm
SYSTEM OF OPERATION(S): gas
TYPE OF FIRE: select, full or semi-auto
AMMUNITION DELIVERY BY: 20-round staggered
   cartridge magazine
SERIAL NO.: C-103208

COMMENTS: This BAR is a commercial weapon
primarily developed for law enforcement post-WWI
sales. It was also hoped that there would be sales to
foreign military governments in the post war era. Very
few of these guns were manufactured and far fewer remain today. Only five or six are known to collectors in
this country. This gun has been test-fired only by former
owners and will probably never be fired again. Note that
the muzzle is fitted with a Cutts compensator. This is
a device that ports the explosive gasses through the
slots in the side, offsetting the gun's natural inclination
to climb. This monitor is one of the rarest and most
sought-after of all collectable automatic firearms in the
world today.

NAME: Browning Automatic Rifle
MODEL: 1919
CALIBER: .30-06
COUNTRY: U.S.A.
MANUFACTURER: Colt Fire Arms Mfg. Co.
CYCLIC RATE OF FIRE: 500 rpm
SYSTEM OF OPERATION(S): gas
TYPE OF FIRE: selective
AMMUNITION DELIVERY BY: 20-round magazine
SERIAL NO.: C-101210

COMMENTS: The 1919 BAR was primarily a commercial venture attempting to secure foreign military
sales. To this extent the effort fell short, as in 1919 few
countries wanted to rearm after WWI. Very few of these
guns were sold. The 1919 model is a very rare
automatic weapon, with probably no more than 200
ever produced.

NAME: Browning Light Machine Gun
MODEL: 1919-A6
CALIBER: .30-06
COUNTRY: U.S.A.
MANUFACTURER: various military contractors
CYCLIC RATE OF FIRE: 550 rpm
SYSTEM OF OPERATION(S): recoil
TYPE OF FIRE: full auto only
AMMUNITION DELIVERY BY: web belt 250-round
   capacity
SERIAL NO.: 177345AC

COMMENTS: This 1919-A6 is an adaptation of the
A-4 Browning using a shorter barrel and adapted with
a bipod, carrying handle and buttstock.

NAME: Johnson Light Machine Gun
MODEL: 1941
CALIBER: .30-06
COUNTRY: U.S.A.
MANUFACTURER: Johnson Automatic, Inc.
CYCLIC RATE OF FIRE: 450-750 rpm
SYSTEM OF OPERATION(S): recoil
TYPE OF FIRE: selective
AMMUNITION DELIVERY BY: 20 cartridge single
   column magazine
SERIAL NO.: 2547

COMMENTS: This machine gun was invented by
Capt. Melvin M. Johnson, U.S. Marine Corps, retired
and was used in our military primarily by the Marine
Corps. It was ingenious in its buffer system and short
recoiling operating mechanism. It fired semi-automatic
from a closed bolt, which insured good accuracy and
fired full automatic from an opened locking bolt which
gave cooling between bursts. It further employed a
rather unique loading system in which the magazine,
which fed from the side, could be expended through
firing and at the same time, without moving the
magazine, be reloaded from five-round clips pushed in
from the right side of the gun. The operator never had
to remove the magazine, thus putting himself out of
service while reloading. The Johnson Gun never saw
extensive military use, as only 5000 were delivered. It
was obviously copied by the Germans resulting in the
FG-42, probably the world's finest and most efficient
assault rifle in large caliber. The Johnson saw limited
use in Israel and other far eastern countries, manufactured under license.

NAME: U.S. Aircraft Cannon
MODEL: MK-12, (Model "O")
CALIBER: 20mm
COUNTRY: U.S.A.
MANUFACTURER: various military contractors
CYCLIC RATE OF FIRE: 600 rpm
SYSTEM OF OPERATION(S): gas
TYPE OF FIRE: full auto only
AMMUNITION DELIVERY BY: disintegrating steel
   link belt
SERIAL NO.: 518042

COMMENTS: The MK-12 Model "O" was a later revision of the famous Hispano-Suiza machine cannon and
was highly successful in use against aircraft and
ground targets alike. It was capable of firing a variety
of explosive, incendiary and armor-piercing projectiles.

NAME: U.S. Aircraft Cannon
MODEL: M-3
CALIBER: 20mm
COUNTRY: U.S.A.
MANUFACTURER: various military contractors
CYCLIC RATE OF FIRE: 600 rpm
SYSTEM OF OPERATION(S): gas
TYPE OF FIRE: full auto
AMMUNITION DELIVERY BY: disintegrating steel
   link belt
SERIAL NO.: 5219

COMMENTS: This M-3 U.S. Aircraft Cannon is an
adaptation of the Hispano-Suiza cannon used in our
military aircraft during WWII. It also was employed by
the British on *Spitfires* and other fighters. Popularity of
this cannon continued on through the Korean War.

NAME: Browning Water-Cooled Heavy Machine Gun
MODEL: 1918
CALIBER: .50
COUNTRY: U.S.A.
MANUFACTURER: Colt Firearms
CYCLIC RATE OF FIRE: 500 rpm
SYSTEM OF OPERATION(S): recoil
TYPE OF FIRE: full auto only
AMMUNITION DELIVERY BY: disintegrating steel
link belt
SERIAL NO.: C-1952W

COMMENTS: This firearm was one of the first .50
caliber machine guns developed and manufactured by
Browning.

NAME: Browning Water-Cooled Heavy Machine Gun
MODEL: M-21, shown on an M-3 anti-aircraft tripod
CALIBER: .50
COUNTRY: U.S.A.
MANUFACTURER: Colt Fire Arms
CYCLIC RATE OF FIRE: 600 rpm of sustained
continuous fire with circulating water cooling
SYSTEM OF OPERATION(S): recoil
TYPE OF FIRE: full auto only
AMMUNITION DELIVERY BY: canisters of linked
belted ammunition
SERIAL NO.: 755387

COMMENTS: The M-21 saw extensive service
through WWII as one of our prime defensive military
firearms.

NAME: Browning Heavy Machine Gun
MODEL: M2-HB
CALIBER: .50
COUNTRY: U.S.A.
MANUFACTURER: various military contractors
CYCLIC RATE OF FIRE: 500-1000 rpm
SYSTEM OF OPERATION(S): recoil
TYPE OF FIRE: full auto only
AMMUNITION DELIVERY BY: disintegrating steel
belt
SERIAL NO.: B-1083821

COMMENTS: This gun is commonly found in dual
and also in quad mounts where heavier fire delivery is
demanded. One of the better designed features of the
HB model is its quick-change barrel which can be taken
off and replaced with a cool barrel after the one in use
becomes too hot to be serviceable. The HB model saw
service through WWII and remains the primary heavy
machine gun of the U.S. and most of the NATO Allies.

NAME: Browning Heavy Machine Gun
MODEL: M2-HB
CALIBER: .50
COUNTRY: U.S.A.
MANUFACTURER: various military contractors
CYCLIC RATE OF FIRE: 550-1000 rpm
SYSTEM OF OPERATION(S): recoil
TYPE OF FIRE: full auto only
AMMUNITION DELIVERY BY: disintegrating steel
belt
SERIAL NO.: N/A

COMMENTS: This gun is commonly found in dual
and also in quad mounts where heavier fire delivery is
demanded. One of the better designed features of the
HB model is its quick-change barrel which can be taken
off and replaced with a cool barrel after the one in use
becomes too hot to be serviceable. The HB model saw
service through WWII and remains the primary heavy
machine gun of the U.S. and most of the NATO Allies.

NAME: Browning Heavy Machine Gun
MODEL: M2-HB
CALIBER: .50
COUNTRY: U.S.A.
MANUFACTURER: various military contractors
CYCLIC RATE OF FIRE: 550-1000 rpm
SYSTEM OF OPERATION(S): recoil
TYPE OF FIRE: full auto only
AMMUNITION DELIVERY BY: disintegrating steel
belt
SERIAL NO.: N/A

COMMENTS: This gun is commonly found in dual
and also in quad mounts where heavier fire delivery is
demanded. One of the better designed features of the
HB model is its quick-change barrel which can be taken
off and replaced with a cool barrel after the one in use
becomes too hot to be serviceable. The HB model saw
service through WWII and remains the primary heavy
machine gun of the U.S. and most of the NATO Allies.

NAME: Browning Heavy Machine Gun
MODEL: M2-HB
CALIBER: .50
COUNTRY: U.S.A.
MANUFACTURER: various military contractors
CYCLIC RATE OF FIRE: 550-1000 rpm
SYSTEM OF OPERATION(S): recoil
TYPE OF FIRE: full auto only
AMMUNITION DELIVERY BY: disintegrating steel belt
SERIAL NO.: N/A

COMMENTS: This gun is commonly found in dual and also in quad mounts where heavier fire delivery is demanded. One of the better designed features of the HB model is its quick-change barrel which can be taken off and replaced with a cool barrel after the one in use becomes too hot to be serviceable. The HB model saw service through WWII and remains the primary heavy machine gun of the U.S. and most of the NATO Allies.

NAME: Browning Heavy Machine Gun Aircraft Type
MODEL: M-3
CALIBER: .50
COUNTRY: U.S.A.
MANUFACTURER: various military contractors
CYCLIC RATE OF FIRE: 1100 rpm
SYSTEM OF OPERATION(S): recoil
TYPE OF FIRE: full auto only
AMMUNITION DELIVERY BY: disintegrating steel link belt
SERIAL NO.: 494927

COMMENTS: This is an adaption of the standard Browning M-2 employing a muzzle booster assembly and a high-speed bumper assembly to promote a higher cyclic rate, primarily for aircraft and anti-aircraft use.

NAME: Browning Water-Cooled Machine Gun
MODEL: 1919
CALIBER: .30-06
COUNTRY: U.S.A.
MANUFACTURER: Colt Patent Fire Arms Mfg. Co.
CYCLIC RATE OF FIRE: 550 rpm
SYSTEM OF OPERATION(S): recoil
TYPE OF FIRE: full auto only
AMMUNITION DELIVERY BY: fabric web belt
SERIAL NO.: C-100257 and C-100258

COMMENTS: The Model 1919 was a post WWI gun from Colt in an attempt to secure foreign military markets and local law enforcement sales. To this extent the effort was nearly a complete failure as the military had all of the weapons it needed, and the law enforcement people were not interested in this heavy weapon. As such, very few of the guns were made. The two model 1919s on display here represent two of the three known in the U.S.A. Equally interesting to the collector is that these two sister guns have consecutive serial numbers, making the pair extremely rare. The guns are mounted on equally rare 1919 tripods which were unique to this model.

NAME: Browning .30 Caliber Water-Cooled Machine Gun
MODEL: 1917-A1
CALIBER: .30-06
COUNTRY: U.S.A.
MANUFACTURER: various military contractors
CYCLIC RATE OF FIRE: 550-600 rpm
SYSTEM OF OPERATION(S): recoil
TYPE OF FIRE: full auto only
AMMUNITION DELIVERY BY: 250-round canvas web belt
SERIAL NO.: 791009 and 791008

COMMENTS: This weapon, John M. Browning's second successful military design, is probably the most famous of all American machine guns known up to the present time. The model 1917 saw limited usage in WWI and was the mainstay of all of our fronts through WWII. The gun's accuracy and dependability is a credit to the genius that John M. Browning bestowed on its design. The gunner could deliver accurate single shots, short bursts or continuous fire. It is here displayed on its 1917-A1 tripod and shown also mounted to its steam hose and condensation can. (This gun is one of a pair of consecutive serial numbered guns in this display).

NAME: Browning Light Machine Gun
MODEL: 1919-A4
CALIBER: .30-06
COUNTRY: U.S.A.
MANUFACTURER: various military contractors
CYCLIC RATE OF FIRE: 550-600 rpm
SYSTEM OF OPERATION(S): recoil
TYPE OF FIRE: full auto only
AMMUNITION DELIVERY BY: fabric web belt of 250-round capacity
SERIAL NO.: 128SAC

COMMENTS: This machine gun has seen continual U.S. military use since its conception. It was an adaptation of the 1917 water-cooled version, and lightened for infantry use. It was widely used by all U.S. military services in all theaters of action.

NAME: Browning Heavy Machine Gun
MODEL: M-2
CALIBER: .50
COUNTRY: U.S.A.
MANUFACTURER: Savage Arms Corp.
CYCLIC RATE OF FIRE: 550-650 rpm
SYSTEM OF OPERATION(S): recoil
TYPE OF FIRE: full auto only
AMMUNITION DELIVERY BY: disintegrating steel link belt
SERIAL NO.: 5, 2, others by various manufacturers

COMMENTS: The M-2 was the principal heavy machine gun of WWII with all the allied nations. It is probably the most commonly found heavy machine gun in the world. It is often copied by other countries and adapted for their own cartridges and calibers. The .50 caliber Browning is one of John M. Browning's finest creations. The gun was developed on the orders of General Pershing who foresaw the need for heavier machine guns to combat greater armor being put into the field by the military. It was found that the French 11mm round was inadequate for the purposes intended, and later a new cartridge was developed, somewhat copying the 13.2mm German anti-tank round. From this the now famous .50 caliber Browning round has developed. This gun has an exceptionally low serial number and was acquired from the Savage Arms Museum.

NAME: Browning Aircraft Light Machine Gun
MODEL: AN-M2
CALIBER: .30-06
COUNTRY: U.S.A.
MANUFACTURER: Buffalo Arms Corp., U.S.A.
CYCLIC RATE OF FIRE: 2000 rpm
SYSTEM OF OPERATION(S): recoil
TYPE OF FIRE: full auto only
AMMUNITION DELIVERY BY: disintegrating steel metal link belt
SERIAL NO.: 38051 and 106295

COMMENTS: This is a Browning flexible-mount machine gun employing a Navy twin mount which was used in the backseat of SBD dive-bomber aircraft of WWII fame. It was primarily used as a defensive weapon, but could be put to good use in strafing ground targets as well. It had a wide sweep of fire and was very lethal, putting out over 2000-rounds per minute in continuous burst fire. Twin mounts similar to this were also used in the nose of the PBY patrol bomber.

NAME: Browning Aircraft Light Machine Gun
MODEL: AN-M2
CALIBER: .30-06
COUNTRY: U.S.A.
MANUFACTURER: Buffalo Arms Corp., U.S.A.
CYCLIC RATE OF FIRE: 1200 rpm
SYSTEM OF OPERATION(S): recoil
TYPE OF FIRE: full auto only
AMMUNITION DELIVERY BY: disintegrating steel metal link belt
SERIAL NO.: 187656

COMMENTS: This Browning AN-M2 is mounted on a standard navy aircraft mount. This was a swivel gun used by aircraft observers or gunners as a defensive weapon from a turret or an open cockpit. This unique mount is equipped with a spring-loaded recoiling system which adds accuracy to the weapon.

NAME: Browning Light Maching Gun
MODEL: AN-M2 Sales Demonstrator
SERIAL NO.: none

NAME: AN-M2 Sales Demonstrator
SERIAL NO.: none

NAME: Browning Light Machine Gun
MODEL: AN-M2
CALIBER: .30-06
COUNTRY: U.S.A.
MANUFACTURER: various U.S. contracts
CYCLIC RATE OF FIRE: 1000 rpm
SYSTEM OF OPERATION(S): recoil
TYPE OF FIRE: full auto only
AMMUNITION DELIVERY BY: disintegrating steel belt
SERIAL NO.: 193561

COMMENTS: This machine gun was designed as an aircraft weapon by revising and lightening the standard model 1919 Browning. All internal parts were lightened and polished and all efforts were made to produce a very high cyclic rate. The AN-M2 (AN means Army-Navy Model M2) was our early fighter armament, also being mounted in bombers. It was also used in dual mounts in swivel positions where the gunner had control of both guns. The M2 was the principal machine gun of the U.S.A.A.F. and RAF prior to and throughout WWII.

NAME: Browning Aircraft Light Machine Gun
MODEL: AN-M2
CALIBER: .30-06
COUNTRY: U.S.A.
MANUFACTURER: Buffalo Arms Corp., U.S.A.
CYCLIC RATE OF FIRE: 1000 rpm
SYSTEM OF OPERATION(S): recoil
TYPE OF FIRE: full auto only
AMMUNITION DELIVERY BY: disintegrating steel metal link belt
SERIAL NO.: 68754

COMMENTS: This is a U.S. Army Air Force adaptation of the .30 caliber Browning Light Aircraft Machine Gun fitted with double spade grips and thumb trigger, prior to and through WWII. This machine gun was commonly mounted on a swivel-type base or Scarff ring where the aircraft gunner could sweep from side to side to defend his aircraft from enemy fighters.

NAME: United Defense Sub-machine Gun
MODEL: 1942
CALIBER: 9mm
COUNTRY: U.S.A.
MANUFACTURER: Marlin Firearms Co., U.S.A.
CYCLIC RATE OF FIRE: 700 rpm
SYSTEM OF OPERATION(S): recoil
TYPE OF FIRE: selective
AMMUNITION DELIVERY BY: 20-round two position feed box magazine
SERIAL NO.: 11338

COMMENTS: Only 15,000 of these weapons were manufactured and most were delivered to the Office of Strategic Services where they were assumed to be shipped to the far East and Europe, though some went to the Dutch West Indies. The UD 42 was a well-engineered sub-machine gun, but it failed to gain military acceptance. Some were supplied with back-to-back 20-round magazines, providing a 40-round capacity. This specimen is most probably the finest known in the U.S. today of the handful surviving.

NAME: U.S. Carbine
MODEL: M-2
CALIBER: .30 Carbine
COUNTRY: U.S.A.
MANUFACTURER: Plainfield Machine Co.
CYCLIC RATE OF FIRE: 600 rpm
SYSTEM OF OPERATION(S): gas
TYPE OF FIRE: selective
AMMUNITION DELIVERY BY: 15- or 30-round box magazine
SERIAL NO.: 1054A

COMMENTS: The U.S. Military Carbine M-2 is a redesigned and modified M-1 Carbine converted to semi and full automatic fire. In this version it was usually provided with a 30-round magazine instead of the standard 15-round issued to the M-1. The M-2 was issued to nearly all of our armed forces and saw action in all theaters of WWII.

NAME: U.S. Sub-machine Gun
MODEL: M-3 *(Grease Gun)*
CALIBER: .45 ACP
COUNTRY: U.S.A.
MANUFACTURER: Guidelamp Division of General Motors
CYCLIC RATE OF FIRE: 350-450 rpm
SYSTEM OF OPERATION(S): recoil
TYPE OF FIRE: full auto
AMMUNITION DELIVERY BY: 30-round staggered box magazine
SERIAL NO.: 143676

COMMENTS: The *Grease Gun* was made in large numbers and issued to the U.S. military in WWII. It supplemented the heavier Thompson, and though quite unpopular it was still an effective and efficient machine gun. Its relatively slow rate of fire was an advantage in that the soldier did not expand his full magazine, thus leaving ammo for subsequent use. An ugly duckling in the field, it was either hated or loved by those who possessed it.

NAME: U.S. Sub-machine Gun
MODEL: M3-A1 *(Grease Gun)*
CALIBER: .45 ACP
COUNTRY: U.S.A.
MANUFACTURER: Guidelamp Division of General
Motors, U.S.A.
CYCLIC RATE OF FIRE: 350-450 rpm
SYSTEM OF OPERATION(S): recoil
TYPE OF FIRE: full auto only
AMMUNITION DELIVERY BY: 30-round staggered
box magazine
SERIAL NO.: 645725

COMMENTS: The M3-A1 *Grease Gun* was a revision of the M-3, incorporating changes in the bolt and the bolt opening procedure. This gun superceded the old M-3 after WWII and was used primarily in the tank corps. The M3-A1 is a rare sub-machine gun due to the fact that none were ever issued to foreign countries. There are probably no more than a dozen original M3-A1s in private collections.

NAME: Reising Sub-machine Gun
MODEL: M-50
CALIBER: .45 ACP
COUNTRY: U.S.A.
MANUFACTURER: Harrington & Richardson,
U.S.A.
CYCLIC RATE OF FIRE: 650 rpm
SYSTEM OF OPERATION(S): recoil
TYPE OF FIRE: selective
AMMUNITION DELIVERY BY: 12- or 20-round
magazine
SERIAL NO.: S-5513

COMMENTS: This Reising M-50 is a full military model. Most military versions were issued to the Marine Corps during WWII. The guns were originally furnished with a 12-round magazine, but these being inadequate, were later furnished with 20-round magazines. A small spike bayonet was also included for use in close combat. Basically, the Reising was a dependable and accurate sub-machine gun. However, it obtained a bad reputation due to political problems of competing companies. Subsequently the Reising was sold in large numbers to law enforcement agencies, as it was a low-cost gun and most agencies could afford it. Presently, a majority of M-50s that haven't been destroyed are in the hands of collectors and shooters who enjoy them in shooting sports and on their walls as prize collector items. The military model is especially desirable, as only a few have survived. This particular specimen is brand new, unfired, in mint condition.

NAME: Reising Sub-machine Gun
MODEL: M-50, Civilian
CALIBER: .45 ACP
COUNTRY: U.S.A.
MANUFACTURER: Harrington & Richardson,
U.S.A.
CYCLIC RATE OF FIRE: 700 rpm
SYSTEM OF OPERATION(S): recoil
TYPE OF FIRE: select, full or semi-auto
AMMUNITION DELIVERY BY: 20-round double
staggered magazine
SERIAL NO.: 7063

COMMENTS: The Reising M-50 Civilian Model was primarily manufactured for law enforcement. It is a well-made, reliable, and accurate sub-machine gun, and regardless of its reputation it is probably the most accurate sub-machine gun manufactured in the post-WWII was era. This is due to the fact that it is about the only one that fires from a closed bolt.

NAME: U.S. Reising Sub-machine Gun
MODEL: Model 55
CALIBER: .45 ACP
COUNTRY: U.S.A.
MANUFACTURER: Harrington & Richardson,
U.S.A.
CYCLIC RATE OF FIRE: 700 rpm
SYSTEM OF OPERATION(S): recoil
TYPE OF FIRE: select, full or semi-auto
AMMUNITION DELIVERY BY: 12 or 20-round
boxed magazine
SERIAL NO.: 65492

COMMENTS: The Model 55 Reising was manufactured strictly for military usage. Most were issued to the Marine Corps, where they saw action in the South Pacific in WWII. Though the function of the gun was quite satisfactory, it was prone to stoppages due to dirt and contamination. It was provided with a wire folding stock that was not satisfactory. The M-55 is one of the rarest sub-machine guns known. This specimen and two others are all of those known in the U.S. This was the only Reising that was not provided with a compensator on the front of the barrel.

NAME: Movie Prop MP-40
MODEL: Reising M-50 (redesigned to look like a
German MP-40)
CALIBER: blanks only
COUNTRY: U.S.A.
MANUFACTURER: High Standard Modified by
MGM, U.S.A.
CYCLIC RATE OF FIRE: 600 rpm adapted for
blank ammunition only
SYSTEM OF OPERATION(S): recoil
TYPE OF FIRE: selective
AMMUNITION DELIVERY BY: 20-round staggered
ammunition box magazine
SERIAL NO.: 1445

COMMENTS: This was one of two M-50 Reisings purchased from the MGM automatic weapons collection. It was used to supplement a lack of original German MP-40 sub-machine guns in movie making. Though the gun only slightly resembles a ''Schmeisser'', at a distance it served the purpose.

THE THOMPSON MACHINE GUN COLLECTION

There are twenty Thompson sub-machine guns in the J. Curtis Earl Collection, and the presence of one weapon in such quantity and diversity demands separate explanation. The Thompson was the very first and by far the most famous and recognized American sub-machine gun. The collection here is unequalled.

The Thompson is one of the finest mechanisms ever put into a firearm, and one of the most historically intriguing. Its quality was, in fact, the reason for its demise in military issue, for even the latest, relatively crude M-1A1 guns took considerable production time and cost $45-50 in World War II, when the Army wanted a gun costing 20-30% of that figure.

The Thompson had the misfortune to arrive on the market in 1921, when military establishments simply weren't buying anything, and legitimate enterprises or less-developed countries could purchase surplus weapons for very little money. However, it was prohibition time in America, and some gentlemen in the illegal liquor business occasionally felt a great need to deal with their competition in a resolute manner. There were also people who had land matters to settle, banks from which to make unauthorized withdrawals, and political disputes to negotiate. Thus, the Thompson became associated with bloodthirsty villians, the weapon of the strikebreaking goon and the Irish insurrectionist, of John Dillinger and Machine Gun Kelly, of troublemakers in general and rumrunners in particular. And none of this provided enough revenue to make Auto Ordnance very profitable.

Having entered the firearms business in 1916, John Tagliaferro Thompson, retired Army general and former Ordnance Board member, also pursued a smaller "trench broom" designed for close-in attacks. They opted to use a lock/delay system conceived and patented by John Blish, an H-shaped bronze wedge whose friction against its steel trackway provided sufficient delay to assure a pressure drop before the breech opened. Though called a lock, this mechanism was really a delay device, and was standard in all the '21 and '28 series Thompsons. It performed a mechanical function somewhat analagous to a hinge, and despite the apochryphal tales, these guns would not function with the lock physically removed.

Thompsons belong to three major and several minor groups. The first consists of the original lot of guns made by Colt in 1921. A little over 15,000 were manufactured, of which perhaps 10% still exist in the United States. Any Thompson which bears the Colt name is or was a 1921 Model. This gun fired normally at 750-850 rounds per minute, though some older, well-worn guns have self-polished themselves or have been modified to shoot even faster. The military felt this rate was impractically high, and the actuator, buffer, and associated parts were modified in small lots sold as 1928 Models. In 1939, running out of Thompsons, Auto Ordnance tried to get Colt and Savage to make more to supply the Allied war effort. Colt refused, and so did Savage at first, but later relented. The guns Savage and, later, Auto Ordnance produced are mechanically identical to the 1928 models ordered by the Navy 13 years before, and cycle at about 550-650 rounds per minute. The generations and variations through which these two early models passed are discussed accompanying the specimens in the collection. It must be noted, however, that the Savage and Auto Ordnance guns were not as beautifully made as the Model 1921s, and as production progressed, features were simplified, markings changed, and the guns generally cheapened.

The M-1 series is entirely different and has very few items in common with the earlier gun. It is a straight blowback design, using a heavier bolt. Details and variants are explained with the guns. At the time the M-1 series was produced, a 30-round magazine was introduced to replace the 20-round unit as standard. These guns were never fitted to accept drum magazines, and their grip frames delete the cutouts. It is reported that some M-1A1s were modified to accept drums, but this appears to have been done long after their military service.

The main magazine of the Roaring Twenties was, of course, the 50-round drum. The larger, even slower-loading 100-round 'C' drum was not terribly popular even with the Capone enforcers, since its bulk and weight and, some say, tendency toward jams made it awkward. The 20-round box magazine was standard. There was also a special 18-round magazine called the XVIII, designed for the riot control shot cartridge, a slightly longer round which necessitated a longer horizontal span.

Hollywood fantasy movies made the "Tommy Gun" seem far more ubiquitous and dangerous than it ever really was. Auto Ordnance did, however, adopt and copyright as a trademark the nickname "Tommy Gun", and so marked some guns. Thompsons were purchased steadily in tiny quantities by brigands, governments, smaller agencies of the United States Government (the Post Office was first) and law enforcement agencies. In the Midwest, where bank robbery became almost an epidemic, police felt compelled to own a Thompson or two, frequently supplemented by a light machine gun and/or a heavy machine gun.

France placed the first big order in 1939, requesting 3,750 guns. In the twenty years preceding, the U.S. Army had ordered fewer than 400, though the Army and Marines inherited most of those ordered by other government agencies. The Army requested 900 more before the end of 1939. The British were the largest overseas customers for the 1928A1. All told, about 1.75 million were produced of all models.

It was a long, long trip from the 'tape' fed prototypes of 1919 to the relatively crude but businesslike M-1A1. The guns, with their sheet metal, padded oiler devices in the M1928s and '21s, and the massive construction of the M-1 series, proved especially reliable in humid tropical climates, and while they had some problems with sand and were surely very heavy, the guns established an enviable reputation for overall dependability. They were made of excellent materials, and almost never broke. They were also more accurate than most sub-machine guns, partly due to their bulk and mechanical stability-some say due to the compensators used to vent gasses upward on most of the earlier models. The Cutts compensator was introduced to the guns in 1926, and appears in considerable variety.

These guns represent their times, and not just in the military sense. They are American products, beautifully made, whose quality no sane man questioned, and whose deadliness was as obvious as their beauty. The myth may be bigger than reality, but the reality is legendary.

NAME: Thompson Sub-machine Gun
MODEL: 1921-A (Early)
CALIBER: .45 ACP
COUNTRY: U.S.A.
MANUFACTURER: Colt Patent Firearms Co.
CYCLIC RATE OF FIRE: 800 rpm
SYSTEM OF OPERATION(S): recoil
TYPE OF FIRE: full and semi-auto
AMMUNITION DELIVERY BY: various box and drum magazines
SERIAL NO.: 611

COMMENTS: John T. Thompson and several other engineers and financial backers formed the Auto-Ordnance Corp. prior to WWI to develop an automatic rifle. Not successful in this endeavor, they turned their attention to producing a "Trench Broom" after the war. Since there were no trenches left to be swept, Thompson coined the new gun "The Thompson Sub-machine Gun" of 1921. Colt produced the major parts of the new gun and Auto-Ordnance assembled the pieces.

NAME: Thompson Sub-machine Gun
MODEL: 1921-AC (Midas Thompson)
CALIBER: .45 ACP
COUNTRY: U.S.A.
MANUFACTURER: Colt Patent Firearms Co.
CYCLIC RATE OF FIRE: 800 rpm
SYSTEM OF OPERATION(S): recoil
TYPE OF FIRE: selective
AMMUNITION DELIVERY BY: various box and drum magazine
SERIAL NO.: 1361

COMMENTS: Curtis Earl purchased this gun many years ago, sold it twice, and bought it back so it is now a permanent part of this complete Thompson collection. The engraving is 24 ct. gold inlay and was custom engraved by Colt's chief engraver, Mr. Earl Bieu. This Thompson has experienced widespread publicity throughout the world and is well known to collectors of fine weapons everywhere.

NAME: Thompson Sub-machine Gun
MODEL: 1921-A (Late model)
CALIBER: .45 ACP
COUNTRY: U.S.A.
MANUFACTURER: Colt Patent Firearms Co.
CYCLIC RATE OF FIRE: 800 rpm
SYSTEM OF OPERATION(S): recoil
TYPE OF FIRE: selective
AMMUNITION DELIVERY BY: various box and drum magazines
SERIAL NO.: 9077

COMMENTS: 15,023 model 1921s were built by Colt, but Thompson and Auto-Ordnance were not successful in marketing the guns. Adverse publicity was generated when the Capone mob and other anti-social elements began using the guns to settle their differences. However, in 1926 the U.S. Post Office ordered 250 to issue to Marines guarding mail shipments. The Marines enjoyed the gun and took it with them to Nicaragua and in 1927 to Shanghai. From these two military excursions the U.S. Navy ordered Thompsons to their specifications, which were altered 1921 models.

NAME: Thompson Sub-machine Gun
MODEL: 1921-A1
CALIBER: .45 ACP
COUNTRY: U.S.A.
MANUFACTURER: Colt Patent Firearms Co.
CYCLIC RATE OF FIRE: 800 rpm
SYSTEM OF OPERATION(S): recoil
TYPE OF FIRE: selective
AMMUNITION DELIVERY BY: various box and
  drum magazine
SERIAL NO.: 3873

COMMENTS: This Colt Thompson is very unusual, and it is most probably a prototype military gun. As the exact history is unknown, we can only speculate that the model number 1921-A1 was used for testing. Only two such guns are known to exist.

NAME: Thompson Carbine
MODEL: 1927
CALIBER: .45 ACP
COUNTRY: U.S.A.
MANUFACTURER: Colt Patent Firearms Co.
CYLIC RATE OF FIRE:
SYSTEM OF OPERATION(S): recoil
TYPE OF FIRE: semi-auto only
AMMUNITION DELIVERY BY: various box and
  drum magazines
SERIAL NO.: 5252

COMMENTS: The model 1927 Thompson Carbine is one of the rarest Colt guns in the world. Only 42 were registered, and of those only 17 are known to exist. This gun was obtained by Curtis Earl from the Arizona State Prison. It was primarily designed to serve as a bank guard gun or for personal guard protection where a sub-machine gun was deemed unadvisable.

NAME: Thompson Sub-machine Gun
MODEL: 1921-8 (U.S. Navy Model)
CALIBER: .45 ACP
COUNTRY: U.S.A.
MANUFACTURER: Colt Patent Firearms Co.
CYCLIC RATE OF FIRE: 600 rpm
SYSTEM OF OPERATION(S): recoil
TYPE OF FIRE: selective
AMMUNITION DELIVERY BY: various box and
  drum magazine
SERIAL NO.: 10398

COMMENTS: In 1928 Colt modified a number of model 1921 AC Thompsons to comply with orders from the U.S. Navy Dept. for a Thompson firing no faster than 600-rounds per minute. To accomplish this, Colt revised the 21 by adding a heavier actuator, a smaller recoiling main spring and a completely different buffer and buffer pilot assembly. With very few exceptions all Navy guns were supplied with either number two or number three compensators.

NAME: Thompson Sub-machine Gun
MODEL: 1921-8 U.S. Navy (original contract)
CALIBER: .45 ACP
COUNTRY: U.S.A.
MANUFACTURER: Colt Patent Firearms Co.
CYCLIC RATE OF FIRE: 600 rpm
SYSTEM OF OPERATION(S): recoil
TYPE OF FIRE: selective
AMMUNITION DELIVERY BY: various box and
  drum magazine
SERIAL NO.: 7805

COMMENTS: This Navy Thompson was purchased from the New York State Prisons system where it was a guard gun at Sing Sing. It is one of the original Navy contract guns as evidenced by its two-piece actuator riveted together. The horizontal forend with its Enfield-type sling swivels are indicative of the original contract by the U.S. Navy in 1928.

NAME: Thompson Sub-machine Gun (cased set)
MODEL: 1921-28
CALIBER: .45 ACP
COUNTRY: U.S.A.
MANUFACTURER: Colt Patent Firearms Co.
CYCLIC RATE OF FIRE: 600 rpm
SYSTEM OF OPERATION(S): recoil
TYPE OF FIRE: selective
AMMUNITION DELIVERY BY: various box and
  drum magazine
SERIAL NO.: 11284

COMMENTS: This case set is shown as it was purchased from the Department of Police in Montgomery County, Rockville, Maryland. The case is known as the FBI hardcase; which is compartmented for the gun and for each double X or 20-round magazine, plus and L drum magazine holding 50 rounds. The complete original case set exhibited here is extremely rare.

NAME: Thompson Sub-machine Gun
MODEL: 1928-A1 (early military model)
CALIBER: .45 ACP
COUNTRY: U.S.A.
MANUFACTURER: Savage Arms Corp.
CYCLIC RATE OF FIRE: 600 rpm
SYSTEM OF OPERATION(S): recoil
TYPE OF FIRE: selective
AMMUNITION DELIVERY BY: various box and
  drum magazine
SERIAL NO.: S-541758

COMMENTS: This gun shows differences in attempting to cut the cost of manufacturing as far as possible. It is a mint condition example of that effort.

NAME: Thompson Sub-machine Gun
MODEL: 1928-A1 (British)
CALIBER: .45 ACP
COUNTRY: U.S.A.
MANUFACTURER: Savage Arms Corp.
CYCLIC RATE OF FIRE: n/a
SYSTEM OF OPERATION(S): recoil
TYPE OF FIRE: selective
AMMUNITION DELIVERY BY: various box and
  drum magazine
SERIAL NO.: S-257991

COMMENTS: The British put their sling swivels on their forward grip and on the top of the butt stop, contrary to American attachments. This gun also exhibits British proof marks showing that it's been accepted by the British military.

NAME: Thompson Sub-machine Gun
MODEL: 1928-A1 (late model)
CALIBER: .45 ACP
COUNTRY: U.S.A.
MANUFACTURER: Auto Ordnance Corp., U.S.A.
CYCLIC RATE OF FIRE: 600 rpm
SYSTEM OF OPERATION(S): recoil
TYPE OF FIRE: selective
AMMUNITION DELIVERY BY: various box and
  drum magazine
SERIAL NO.: AO-134834

COMMENTS: This Auto Ordnance manufactured Thompson is a mint condition specimen exhibiting WWII manufacturing modifications.

NAME: Thompson Military Sub-machine Gun
  Prototype
MODEL: Experimental
CALIBER: 9mm Parabellum
COUNTRY: U.S.A.
MANUFACTURER: Savage Arms Corp.
CYCLIC RATE OF FIRE: 700 rpm
SYSTEM OF OPERATION(S): recoil
TYPE OF FIRE: selective
AMMUNITION DELIVERY BY: staggered cartridge
  box magazine
SERIAL NO.: S1

COMMENTS: This rare 9mm Thompson was one of only a very few manufactured. This particular model is the only one known to exist in any private collection in the world.

NAME: Thompson Sub-machine Gun
MODEL: M-1
CALIBER: .45 ACP
COUNTRY: U.S.A.
MANUFACTURER: Savage Arms Corp., U.S.A.
CYCLIC RATE OF FIRE: 600 rpm
SYSTEM OF OPERATION(S): recoil
TYPE OF FIRE: selective
AMMUNITION DELIVERY BY: box magazine only
SERIAL NO.: 228162

COMMENTS: In an effort to cut production costs on the expensive 1928 model the M-1 was produced which reflected many reduced manufacturing costs. It was also at this point that the box magazine was extended from 20- to 30-rounds, which was supplied with this model Thompson.

NAME: Thompson Sub-machine Gun
MODEL: M1-A1
CALIBER: .45 ACP
COUNTRY: U.S.A.
MANUFACTURER: Savage Arms Corp.
CYCLIC RATE OF FIRE: 600 rpm
SYSTEM OF OPERATION(S): recoil
TYPE OF FIRE: selective
AMMUNITION DELIVERY BY: 30-round box
  magazine
SERIAL NO.: 312966

COMMENTS: The M1-A1 Thompson was a further modification of the model M-1 in an effort to further reduce manufacturing costs. This was a simple operation in which the floating firing pin spring and hammer were eliminated and replaced by a fixed firing pin in the front of the bolt, thus reducing manufacturing costs and creating the M1-A1 model.

NAME: Thompson Sub-machine Gun
MODEL: M1-A1
CALIBER: .45 ACP
COUNTRY: U.S.A.
MANUFACTURER: Savage Arms Corp.
CYCLIC RATE OF FIRE: 600 rpm
SYSTEM OF OPERATION(S): recoil
TYPE OF FIRE: selective
AMMUNITION DELIVERY BY: 30-round box
  magazine
SERIAL NO.: 306581

COMMENTS: This particular M1-A1 Thompson is known as the Tanker Model. It has a slight addition to the forend, simply a steel band surrounding the barrel and the forend to prevent breakage in handling or leaving the close confines of a tank. This modification was issued to members of the tank corps only, and in all other respects was a standard M1-A1 Thompson.

NAME: Thompson Sub-machine Gun
MODEL: M1-A1 (presentation model)
CALIBER: .45 ACP
COUNTRY: U.S.A.
MANUFACTURER: Savage Arms Corp.
CYCLIC RATE OF FIRE: 600 rpm
SYSTEM OF OPERATION(S): recoil
TYPE OF FIRE: selective
AMMUNITION DELIVERY BY: 30-round box
  magazine
SERIAL NO.: 85004

COMMENTS: This M1-A1 was purchased from the Savage Arms Museum. It was one of four Thompsons customized by Savage as presentation guns to be delivered to: 1) President of the United States, 2) General Eisenhower, 3) Admiral Nimitz and 4) General MacArthur. For some unknown reason none of these presentation models were delivered. This particular gun reflects the fourth M1-A1 Thompson produced by Savage. Their serial numbering began at 85,000. Just which of these dignitaries this particular gun was designed to go to is clearly speculative.

NAME: Thompson Sub-machine Gun
MODEL: 1928 (commercial)
CALIBER: .45 ACP
COUNTRY: U.S.A.
MANUFACTURER: Savage Arms Corp.
CYCLIC RATE OF FIRE: 600 rpm
SYSTEM OF OPERATION(S): recoil
TYPE OF FIRE: full and semi-auto
AMMUNITION DELIVERY BY: various box and
  drum magazine
SERIAL NO.: S-71189NAC

COMMENTS: Savage Arms purchased the manufacturing rights to the Thompson, and this model 1928 commercial is an example. These guns were manufactured for commercial and military sales. The first large contract went to England and other foreign countries where they were employed by those countries military organizations.

NAME: Thompson Sub-machine Gun
MODEL: 1928-AC
CALIBER: .45 ACP
COUNTRY: U.S.A.
MANUFACTURER: Colt Patent Firearms Co.
CYCLIC RATE OF FIRE: 600 rpm
SYSTEM OF OPERATION(S): recoil
TYPE OF FIRE: selective
AMMUNITION DELIVERY BY: various box and
  drum magazine
SERIAL NO.: 14

COMMENTS: This Colt Thompson is strangely marked and its history is strictly speculation. The gun is unusual in that it is a 1928-AC marked Colt. The other markings on each part of the gun shows an AOC in a diamond. Later in this gun's history Numric Arms Corp. stamped their initials NAC with a serial number 14. As such it does not fit any other Thompson category. This particular gun with several others were purchased from the Virginia State Police.

NAME: Thompson Sub-machine Gun
MODEL: 1928-AC Colt
CALIBER: .45 ACP
COUNTRY: U.S.A.
MANUFACTURER: Colt Patent Firearms Co.
CYCLIC RATE OF FIRE: 600 rpm
SYSTEM OF OPERATION(S): recoil
TYPE OF FIRE: selective
AMMUNITION DELIVERY BY: various box and
  drum magazines
SERIAL NO.: NAC-15

COMMENTS: This Colt Thompson is unique in that every part is marked with the letter G. Other markings including 1928-AC vary from the normal. This gun was one of several purchased from the Virginia State Police. No other information on the history of this strangely marked gun is available.

NAME: Thompson Sub-machine Gun
MODEL: 1921-A
CALIBER: .45 ACP
COUNTRY: U.S.A.
MANUFACTURER: Colt Patent Firearms Co.
CYCLIC RATE OF FIRE: 800 rpm
SYSTEM OF OPERATION(S): recoil
TYPE OF FIRE: selective
AMMUNITION DELIVERY BY: various box and drum magazines
SERIAL NO.: NAC-2

COMMENTS: This Colt Thompson was purchased form the Virginia State Police and is unusual in that exhibits only Numric Arms Corp. serial numbers, Numric Arms having bought the inventory and tooling from Colt prior to producing its own 1928 model. It is believed this gun (and 22 others) were test guns or an over-run on the original contract of 15,000 guns. All were purchased by Earl from the Virginia State Police.

NAME: FN
MODEL: FAL
CALIBER: 7.62 NATO
COUNTRY: Belgium
MANUFACTURER: FN
CYCLIC RATE OF FIRE: 700 rpm
SYSTEM OF OPERATION(S): gas
TYPE OF FIRE: semi or full auto (optional)
AMMUNITION DELIVERY BY: 20-round box magazine
SERIAL NO.: 001

COMMENTS: The FN FAL has been built under license all over the Western world. Robust, reliable and simple to maintain and operate, the FAL set a new standard when it appeared in 1953 and continues to outshine its competiton. This example is license built with the exclusive serial number 001.

NAME: Madsen
MODEL: M/1950
CALIBER: 9mm
COUNTRY: Denmark
MANUFACTURER: Madsen
CYCLIC RATE OF FIRE: 550 rpm
SYSTEM OF OPERATION(S): blowback
TYPE OF FIRE: full auto
AMMUNITION DELIVERY BY: 32-round box magazine
SERIAL NO.: 1863

COMMENTS: The last of the famous Madsen-produced guns (Madsen no longer produces firearms), the M/50 was a well-made and conventionally-designed sub-machine gun. Its parentage comes from the Swedish firm Husqvarna, which licensed Madsen to build the M/49 and eventually the M/50 and M/53.

NAME: Gewehr 3
MODEL: G-3
CALIBER: 7.62 NATO
COUNTRY: Germany
MANUFACTURER: Heckler & Koch
CYCLIC RATE OF FIRE: 550 rpm
SYSTEM OF OPERATION(S): blowback
TYPE OF FIRE: selective
AMMUNITION DELIVERY BY: 20-round box magazine
SERIAL NO.: 2039

COMMENTS: Developed post WWII based on the MP-44, cheaply made from stampings and plastic, it is nevertheless a functional and effective assault rifle.

NAME: MG-42/59
MODEL: n/a
CALIBER: 7.62 NATO
COUNTRY: W. Germany
MANUFACTURER: Rheinmetall
CYCLIC RATE OF FIRE: 750-1350 rpm depending on modifications
SYSTEM OF OPERATION(S): short recoil
TYPE OF FIRE: selective
AMMUNITION DELIVERY BY: linked metal belt
SERIAL NO.: 7043

COMMENTS: This specimen is basically the same gun as the WWII series, but firing the 7.62mm NATO cartridge.

NAME: MP-K
MODEL: 1963
CALIBER: 9mm
COUNTRY: West Germany
MANUFACTURER: Walther
CYCLIC RATE OF FIRE: approx. 550 rpm
SYSTEM OF OPERATION(S): blowback
TYPE OF FIRE: selective
AMMUNITION DELIVERY BY: 32-round box magazine
SERIAL NO.: 1333

COMMENTS: The Walther MP-K is a blowback weapon using steel stampings for most of its basic structure. The bolt is overhung, the bulk of it above the axis of the barrel and overlapping the breech in its closed position. There is also a longer version, sold in much of the world as a semi-automatic carbine. These guns are used by many S.W.A.T. and anti-terrorist units.

NAME: Uzi
MODEL: n/a
CALIBER: 9mm
COUNTRY: Israel
MANUFACTURER: Israel Military Industries and FN, (Belgium) under license
CYCLIC RATE OF FIRE: 600 rpm
SYSTEM OF OPERATION(S): blowback
TYPE OF FIRE: full auto
AMMUNITION DELIVERY BY: 25-, 32- or 40-round box magazine
SERIAL NO.: 57390

COMMENTS: Designed in the early 1950s based on a Czech design, the Uzi is one of the best sub-machine guns in use today.

NAME: Uzi
MODEL: Mini-Uzi
CALIBER: 9mm
COUNTRY: Israel
MANUFACTURER: Israel Military Industries
CYCLIC RATE OF FIRE: 950 rpm
SYSTEM OF OPERATION(S): blowback
TYPE OF FIRE: full auto
AMMUNITION DELIVERY BY: 20-, 25- or 32-round box magazine
SERIAL NO.: MU03120

COMMENTS: Developed in response for a smaller version, the Mini-Uzi in all respects is identical to the larger Uzi, but is easier to conceal and can be fired with one hand if necessary.

NAME: Franchi
MODEL: LF-57
CALIBER: 9mm
COUNTRY: Italy
MANUFACTURER: Franchi Spa
CYCLIC RATE OF FIRE: 500 rpm
SYSTEM OF OPERATION(S): blowback
TYPE OF FIRE: full auto
AMMUNITION DELIVERY BY: 20- or 40-round box magazine
SERIAL NO.: 0004 SAC

COMMENTS: First produced in 1956 the LF-57's only commercial success was an order from the Italian Navy. Although the Franchi was well designed and competitive to other sub-machine guns of the 1950s, it was never a commercial success.

NAME: Star
MODEL: Z70
CALIBER: 9mm
COUNTRY: Spain
MANUFACTURER: Echeverria SA
CYCLIC RATE OF FIRE: 550 rpm
SYSTEM OF OPERATION(S): blowback
TYPE OF FIRE: selective, semi or full auto
AMMUNITION DELIVERY BY: 20-, 30- or 40-round box magazine
SERIAL NO.: 173031

COMMENTS: The Z70 Star is the product of a long line of Echeverria-produced sub-machine guns which were produced initially in the 1930s and borrowed heavily from German-designed guns, expecially the MP-40. The Z70 was adopted by the Spanish armed forces in the early 1970s and is still current today.

NAME: Carl Gustav
MODEL: M-45B
CALIBER: special high-velocity 9mm
COUNTRY: Sweden
MANUFACTURER: Carl Gustav
CYCLIC RATE OF FIRE: 600 rpm
SYSTEM OF OPERATION(S): blowback
TYPE OF FIRE: full auto
AMMUNITION DELIVERY BY: 36- or 50-round box magazine
SERIAL NO.: 500719

COMMENTS: Lacking a sub-machine gun of their own, the Swedes introduced the M-45 to supply their armed forces. A cheap and simple design, it is well made and has been bought by many countries and was built in Egypt under license where it was called the ''Port Said''. Modified to accept a better magazine in 1948, this version is known as the M-45B.

NAME: Degtyaryov Light Machine Gun
MODEL: RPD
CALIBER: 7.62mm
COUNTRY: U.S.S.R. (China)
MANUFACTURER: State Maufacture
CYCLIC RATE OF FIRE: 700 rpm
SYSTEM OF OPERATION(S): gas
TYPE OF FIRE: full auto
AMMUNITION DELIVERY BY: belt fed from drum
SERIAL NO.: 218245

COMMENTS: The RPD has been the standard light machine gun for the Soviets since the 1950s. This specimen was built under license in the People's Republic of China and is a very late version, probably captured in Vietnam.

NAME: Russian Assault
MODEL: AK-47 (Kalashnikov)
CALIBER: 7.62 by 39mm
COUNTRY: U.S.S.R.
MANUFACTURER: State
CYCLIC RATE OF FIRE: 600 rpm
SYSTEM OF OPERATION(S): gas
TYPE OF FIRE: full auto only
AMMUNITION DELIVERY BY: 30-round curved box magazine
SERIAL NO.: BT4969

COMMENTS: The Kalashnikov displayed here is the folding stock model and considered by many to be the world's finest assault rifle. It is a highly efficient, totally reliable combat infantry weapon.

NAME: Russian Assault
MODEL: Type-56 (Chinese)
CALIBER: 7.62 by 39mm
COUNTRY: U.S.S.R.
MANUFACTURER: State
CYCLIC RATE OF FIRE: 600 rpm
SYSTEM OF OPERATION(S): gas
TYPE OF FIRE: full auto only
AMMUNITION DELIVERY BY: 30-round box magazine
SERIAL NO.: 11078529

COMMENTS: This gun is an average example of the Kalashnikov assault rifles found in Korea and Vietnam. The sample shown here was captured and returned to the U.S. as a war souvenir from the Vietnam conflict.

NAME: Mac-10 Sub-machine Gun
MODEL: M-10
CALIBER: 9mm
COUNTRY: U.S.A.
MANUFACTURER: Militray Armament Corp. of U.S.A.
CYCLIC RATE OF FIRE: 900 rpm
SYSTEM OF OPERATION(S): recoil
TYPE OF FIRE: select, full or semi-auto
AMMUNITION DELIVERY BY: 30-round staggered magazine
SERIAL NO.: 2000457

COMMENTS: This firearm was manufactured at the beginning of the Vietnam War for possible military use. Actually, most guns were sold to law enforcement agencies and private collectors. A good number also belong to the movie industry which use them in TV and movie productions.

NAME: Mini-14 Assault Rifle
MODEL: AC-556-K
CALIBER: 5.56mm
COUNTRY: U.S.A.
MANUFACTURER: Strum-Ruger & Co., U.S.A.
CYCLIC RATE OF FIRE: 700 rpm
SYSTEM OF OPERATION(S): gas
TYPE OF FIRE: selective fire with three-shot burst control
AMMUNITION DELIVERY BY: 20- and 30-round staggered magazines
SERIAL NO.: 191-03371

COMMENTS: This firearm was developed as civilian competition for the M-16 in law enforcement sales. It has been carefully controlled by Ruger to that extent. It is a well made and efficient assault rifle and has been purchased by many law enforcement and prison agencies.

NAME: Assault Rifle
MODEL: M-16
CALIBER: 5.56mm
COUNTRY: U.S.A.
MANUFACTURER: Colt Fire Arms Company
CYCLIC RATE OF FIRE: 700 rpm
SYSTEM OF OPERATION(S): gas
TYPE OF FIRE: selective
AMMUNITION DELIVERY BY: 20- or 30-round staggered magazine
SERIAL NO.: 9052332

COMMENTS: Originally designed by Eugene Stoner in the 1950s, the production rights of the rifle were sold by Armalite to Colt in 1959. Bought initially by smaller Southeast Asian countries, the U.S. Army finally adopted it in the 1960s, issuing it to all areas of operation except NATO where the 7.62 standard cartridge remained standard.

NAME: Assault Rifle, Carbine
MODEL: M-16 CAR
CALIBER: 5.56mm
COUNTRY: U.S.A.
MANUFACTURER: Colt Firearms Company
CYCLIC RATE OF FIRE: 700 rpm
SYSTEM OF OPERATION(S): n/a
TYPE OF FIRE: selective
AMMUNITION DELIVERY BY: 20- or 30-round staggered cartridge magazine
SERIAL NO.: 9271015

COMMENTS: Like its parent, the larger M-16 rifle, the shorty is a very efficient, easy to use, well-controlled, assault rifle. The CAR variant originally was intended for airborne and armored vehicle personnel.

NAME: Armalite Assault Rifle
MODEL: AR-18
CALIBER: 5.56mm
COUNTRY: U.S.A.
MANUFACTURER: Armalite, U.S.A.
CYCLIC RATE OF FIRE: 750 rpm
SYSTEM OF OPERATION(S): gas
TYPE OF FIRE: selective
AMMUNITION DELIVERY BY: 20- or 30-round staggered round box magazines
SERIAL NO.: A5290

COMMENTS: This was a post WWII assault rifle designed by Eugene Stoner, inventor of the M-16. The AR-18 overcame many of the shortcomings of the AR-15 or M-16, and as such is far more reliable in combat conditions.

NAME: Ingram Sub-machine Gun
MODEL: M-6
CALIBER: .45 ACP
COUNTRY: U.S.A.
MANUFACTURER: Police Ordnance Company, U.S.A.
CYCLIC RATE OF FIRE: 600 rpm
SYSTEM OF OPERATION(S): recoil
TYPE OF FIRE: selective
AMMUNITION DELIVERY BY: 30-round staggered box magazine
SERIAL NO.: 16

COMMENTS: The M-6 commercial sub-machine gun was manufactured primarily for law enforcement use, with some consideration given to foreign military or police sales. A number of M-6s have been delivered to police agencies in South America. The gun is well manufactured, but the quality is still substandard to most of our other military and commercially manufactured sub-machine guns. This example has an experimental 16-in. barrel.

NAME: Ingram Sub-machine Gun
MODEL: M-6
CALIBER: .45 ACP
COUNTRY: U.S.A.
MANUFACTURER: Police Ordnance Co., U.S.A.
CYCLIC RATE OF FIRE: 600 rpm
SYSTEM OF OPERATION(S): recoil
TYPE OF FIRE: selective
AMMUNITION DELIVERY BY: 30-round staggered box magazine
SERIAL NO.: 1391

COMMENTS: The M-6 Commercial Submachine Gun was manufactured primarily for law enforcement, with some consideration given to foreign military or police sales. A number of M-6s have been delivered to different police agencies in South America. The gun is fairly well manufactured, but the quality is still substandard to most of our other military and commercially manufactured sub-machine guns.

NAME: Ingram Sub-machine Gun
MODEL: M-6
CALIBER: .45 ACP
COUNTRY: U.S.A.
MANUFACTURER: Police Ordnance Co., U.S.A.
CYLIC RATE OF FIRE: 600 rpm
SYSTEM OF OPERATION(S): recoil
TYPE OF FIRE: select, full or semi-auto
AMMUNITION DELIVERY BY: 30-round box magazine
SERIAL NO.: 01007

COMMENTS: The Model 6 appeared in the 1950s and was sold in limited numbers to various police forces, the Cuban Navy, the Peruvian Army and Thailand forces. The M6 was not a commercial success because the market was still flooded from cheap WWII weapons.

NAME: Smith & Wesson Sub-machine Gun
MODEL: 76
CALIBER: 9mm
COUNTRY: U.S.A.
MANUFACTURER: Smith & Wesson, U.S.A.
CYCLIC RATE OF FIRE: 700 rpm
SYSTEM OF OPERATION(S): recoil
TYPE OF FIRE: full auto only
AMMUNITION DELIVERY BY: 30-rounds staggered magazine
SERIAL NO.: U104

COMMENTS: The M-76 was a stamped, low-cost manufactured law enforcement sub-machine gun for special weapons and tactics use. Only a few thousand were manufactured, and most now reside in law enforcement arsenals and in collectors' cabinets.

NAME: Casull 290 Prototype
MODEL: Prototype
CALIBER: .22 Long Rifle
COUNTRY: U.S.A.
MANUFACTURER: Richard Casull, U.S.A.
CYCLIC RATE OF FIRE: 1200 rpm
SYSTEM OF OPERATION(S): recoil
TYPE OF FIRE: selective
AMMUNITION DELIVERY BY: 290-round drum
 magazine
SERIAL NO.: F

COMMENTS: This gun was developed and hand manufactured by Richard Casull of Salt Lake City, Utah, as a prototype to what later became the American 180 sub-machine gun. The American 180 was a semi-successful gun sold primarily to law enforcement agencies and collectors. It fired too fast to be tremendously efficient, but the semi-automatic fire mode also gave a sustained fire quality that some law enforcement agencies desired. This rare prototype is a beautiful example of the gun maker's art and, as such, is a desirable and valuable collectors item.

NAME: U.S. Light Machine Gun
MODEL: M-60
CALIBER: 7.62 NATO
COUNTRY: U.S.A.
MANUFACTURER: Maremont Corp. U.S.A.
CYCLIC RATE OF FIRE: 550 rpm
SYSTEM OF OPERATION(S): gas
TYPE OF FIRE: full auto only
AMMUNITION DELIVERY BY: disintegrating steel
 link belt
SERIAL NO.: 43

COMMENTS: The M-60 superceded the Browning models 1919 A-4 and A-6 and eventually grew into widespread use throughout all U.S. armed services, including the Air Force. It is the primary light machine gun for all of our military services today. It is truly a dual-purpose weapon, being adaptable for use by the individual on a bipod or if mounted on a tripod as a crew-served gun. This is a very early Maremont-produced M-60 and is in unfired condition.

NAME: Light Machine Gun
MODEL: Model 13 (MG-13)
CALIBER: 7.92mm
COUNTRY: Germany
MANUFACTURER: Rheinische Metallwaren
CYCLIC RATE OF FIRE: 650 rpm
SYSTEM OF OPERATION(S): short recoil
TYPE OF FIRE:
AMMUNITION DELIVERY BY: 25-round box or
 76-round saddle drum magazines
SERIAL NO.: A691

COMMENTS: The MG-13 was a WWI water-cooled Dreyse converted into an air-cooled light machine that was magazine instead of belt fed. When the MG-34 was developed for the German Army, most of the MG-13s were sold to Portugal.

THE FABULOUS "75"

The Magnificent French 75mm Gun, designed in 1897, was undeniably the finest fieldpiece in the world. Germany tried for years to equal or surpass it; others copied it. A weapon of unique mobility and accuracy, it could spit out 15 to 20 rounds a minute. (In a postwar demonstration at Aberdeen Proving Grounds, Maryland, a crack American crew achieved a firing rate of 25 rounds a minute).

This gun is best known as the "French 75" and was at its introduction in 1897 a great novelty. It was the first gun to be fitted with a recoil system: the resulting increase in the rate of fire over previous weapons was dramatic—nearly three times better than its contemporaries. Not only did the stability of the carriage speed the relaying of the piece, but the detachment could remain close to the gun when it was fired, to be ready to reload. Fixed ammunition was not new, but was used to further exploit the quick fire potential.

The "French 75" is a true gun having a long barrel, high muzzle velocity (for its day), and flat trajectory. The breech is a quick action "Nordenfelt" eccentric screw type. The hydraulic recoil system is fitted below the barrel.

The gun developed an initial muzzle velocity of 1,805 feet per second, and its projectile could slam into a target 10,000 feet away at nearly 1,000 feet per second. It fired either a 16-pound shrapnel shell or a 12.3-pound high explosive shell to ranges of 9,100 yards and 9,846 yards, respectively. The shrapnel shell was used almost exclusively by the French and British in the early days of the war. For the "75" each 16-pound casing held 300 lead balls weighing 12 grams each, hardened with antimony and mixed with compressed black powder. The French called the drumfire of their massed '75's *refale*, in which a squall of shrapnel shells was sent exploding to release the balls that shattered the opposing infantry.

INDEX

IN MEMORY

OF MY

TWO GOOD FRIENDS...

JIM BENSON

DWAIN TRENTON

NOTES/ADDITIONS